TH

STRANGEST

FOOTBALL

QUIZ

BOOK

First published in the United Kingdom in 2019 by
Portico
Pavilion Books Group Limited
43 Great Ormond Street
London
WC1N 3HZ

An imprint of Pavilion Books Company Ltd

ISBN 978-1-91162-219-2

A CIP catalogue record for this book is available from the British Library.

10 9 8 7 6 5 4 3 2 1

Reproduction by Mission Productions Ltd, Hong Kong
Printed and bound by Imak Offset, Turkey

This book can be ordered direct from the publisher at www.pavilionbooks.com

THE STRANGEST FOOTBALL QUIZ BOOK

PORTICO

CONTENTS

THE QUESTIONS

1

STREAKERS

Streaking is running naked in public. One of the first episodes on a British football pitch came in the early 1970s when Morecambe visited the Eyrie to play the Eagles in the FA Trophy. A streaker came on at half time. He undressed discreetly and ran across the Bedford Town pitch while carrying his clothes. The home club never reached the Football League, but it had some excellent FA Cup runs. They reached the third round in 1955–56 (losing 2-1 to Arsenal in a replay), the FA Cup fourth round in 1963–64 (after beating Newcastle United 2-1 away) and, two years later, lost 0–3 to Everton in the fourth round.

1 **WHEN** was a streaker first introduced to the Subbuteo football game?
Was it **(A)** May 1960, **(B)** May 1974, **(C)** May 1988, or **(D)** May 2004?

Streaking began at Florida State University in the early 1960s and it quickly spread over a hundred college campuses. Michael D. Grimes found that only 9 per cent of respondents used negative words to describe streaking (e.g. exhibitionists, vulgar people, perverts, etc.) whereas 90 per cent used more positive words (e.g. funseekers, faddists, attention seekers, carefree, uninhibited, etc.). Streaking was seen as an amusement … but it wasn't so funny in December 2004, when a streaker burned his naked body by diving on Dunfermline Athletic's artificial pitch.

2 Four pieces of advice are given in Wiggle's *Guide to Better Streaking* (1974). **WHICH** one of these five suggestions is bogus: **(A)** wear dark glasses, **(B)** treat skin well, **(C)** wear tennis shoes, **(D)** join a gym, and **(E)** wear only a smile?

Hilary had a plan when her local team played Berwick Rangers in March 2002. The 22-year-old redhead wore only black hot pants under a full-length zip-up coat. When play stopped for a free kick, in the 71st minute, she took off her coat, climbed over a barrier and sprinted on to the field wearing only hot pants. Chased by a steward, she ran diagonally across the field, her long red hair flowing behind her, while several players stood with hands on hips. The steward caught up with her and covered her with a jacket. Hilary was what referees call 'an outside agent', anything or anyone entering the field of play without permission.

3 Hilary's home club was in Dumfries and is mentioned in the Bible (Matthew 12:42). **WHAT** is the club's name?

In June 2016 a crowd of hundreds of people (including children) gathered in Cardiff's Castle Square to watch a Wales–England Euro 2016 match on a large TV screen. Suddenly a man in the square took off all his clothes and jumped into the square's fountain. He was arrested by the police and taken through crowds of people while still naked. A number of witnesses claimed that the police had managed the crowd poorly because they'd walked the naked man through Castle Square in full sight of children and adults. England beat Wales 2-1.

4 The Wales goal came from a man who had scored nearly 30 goals for his country at that point. **WHO** is he?

Compared with professional footballers, fans seem to run very slowly when they are naked and on the pitch. Sensible streakers wear trainers or, even better, studded football boots. In January 2006 a fan ran on the field at Bury. The 26-year-old had been drinking with friends and was bet £70 to do a naked streak across the pitch. He did it and then faced punishment.

5 **HOW** much was the streaker's fine at Bury (including court costs) – £169, £369, £569 or £769?

The match was in Florida in March 2008 and the intense heat suited streakers. Only 15 minutes of an under-23 international remained when Tiffany May made her appearance on the pitch during a USA v Honduras Olympic soccer match. The definition of streaking means that all the body parts are exposed, but some streakers do not satisfy that criteria. For instance, May was called a streaker, but she wore a bra and a G-string.

6 **WHICH** magazine signed her for a naked photo shoot?

Mark Roberts is the most prolific streaker in the world. His first naked run was at the 1993 Hong Kong rugby sevens after he'd been drinking, and by 2015 he was the veteran of 400 streaks. In Hong Kong he told a friend, 'Mind me clothes,' and then stripped off. He went on the rugby field, picked up the ball and ran the length of the stadium. He went to jail at times, but it was usually for a few hours or an overnight stay. His streaking injuries included two broken ribs, a broken finger and 21 stitches on the back of his leg. Roberts could peel off his Velcro kit before security officers tackled him. He used his naked body as a billboard (e.g. 'I USE DAZ'), and it gave him added confidence.

7 **(A) WHAT** caption did Mark Roberts have on his bum when he gate-crashed the American Superbowl?
(B) WHY does he do it?

It was very hot at London Road, Peterborough, on 19 August 1975, and the visitors were Cardiff City. At half time a teenage girl took to the field. She was wearing a blouse and bell-bottomed trousers. She didn't wear the blouse for long, though, as she peeled it off over her head. Then she undid her bra and ran around in circles among the players. By this time a policeman had run onto the pitch. He took off his helmet, covered up one of the streaker's breasts and led her gently out of the ground. The *Evening Telegraph* ran a front-page cartoon showing two supporters. 'A good afternoon's entertainment, Albert,' said one man in the cartoon, 'Posh got a point and the streaker had two.' The match ended goalless.

8 **WHAT** is the highest placed finish in the history of Cardiff City?

During a hot weekend in May 2001 a number of streakers interrupted matches. They included a man wearing only a bowler hat at Chesterfield, two runners at Barnet and another during the FA Vase final in Birmingham. That same weekend Don Jackson took a £100 bet that he would streak during the Irish Cup Final. Choosing his moment, Jackson stripped off his clothes but kept on his blue underpants because some young children were nearby. When he reached the pitch Jackson stripped naked and became the centre of attention for 14,000 fans. His running was so fast that two stewards ran into each other in a Keystone Kops moment. He was taken to the police station with only a Glentoran scarf covering his modesty.

9 Don Jackson had Glentoran's motto tattooed on his body. **WHAT** was it?

In March 2004 a male streaker ran on to the Altrincham ground to interrupt a Unibond Cheshire Senior Cup Final. It was a corner-kick to Witton Albion when the streaker appeared and ran around the pitch. Brian Pritchard, playing for Witton Albion, tripped up the streaker and apprehended him. Pritchard was then sent off by the referee for violent conduct. The score was 0-0 at the time, and opponents Woodley Sports went on to win 2-1 in extra time. Pritchard's appeal for wrongful dismissal was upheld by an FA disciplinary commission and the red card was rescinded.

10 **WHAT** was Brian Pritchard's profession?

THE ANSWERS 134

2

MASCOTS

Stuart Drummond spent four years as a cruise ship waiter before becoming a call centre worker and football mascot. In 2002 he stood for the Hartlepool town council, campaigning on behalf of youth employment and the town's football club. Drummond was best known as H'Angus, the Hartlepool United football club mascot, who campaigned in his monkey costume ('Vote For H'Angus'). H'Angus won the election with 5,696 votes to the Labour candidate's 5,174 votes, although only 20 per cent of the electorate voted. Drummond was re-elected in 2005 and 2009 but his post was then abolished. 'I just enjoy standing on the terraces,' said Drummond, when his term as mayor ended. 'You couldn't see much of the game when you were a mascot, which is probably not a bad thing this season.'

1 **HOW** many times since 1930 have West Ham United finished a season as London's top club?

Bradley Lowery lived a short and courageous life as a football mascot in the North East. In 2017 he died at the age of six from a rare and painful childhood cancer called neuroblastoma. Bradley had led out the

England team on one occasion and the Sunderland team several times. He had a special relationship with an England international footballer. At Bradley's funeral his international friend wore an England shirt with the number six (Bradley's age) and the name LOWERY on his back. Lots of replica Sunderland shirts were visible in the funeral procession, and the crowd sang 'There's only one Bradley Lowery.' During the service Father Ian Jackson said, 'Brad was a bright, brave, lovely, cheeky little monkey. He was warm and embracing. He touched the lives of us all.'

2 **WHICH** England international footballer left an England training camp to attend the funeral of Bradley Lowery?

Mascots can be four years old, taking in the atmosphere at a huge stadium, or, like Bernard Jones of Preston, they could have been watching their team for more than 80 seasons. Jones had listened to a radio commentary when Preston North End played Huddersfield Town in the 1938 FA Cup Final. In 2017 Jones was given a mascot's tour of the stadium before being introduced to the first-team squad and Preston manager Alex Neil. The most famous kit man and mascot is possibly Neil Baldwin of Stoke City, who has been described as circus clown and preacher.

3 **(A) WHAT** was the name of the film and autobiography based on Neil Baldwin's life and **(B) WHICH** actor played him in the film? (2)

Mascots are sometimes confrontational towards rival mascots. Nine-foot-tall Cyril the Swan (Swansea) once had a fight with Zampa the Lion (Millwall). Other mascots clap and motivate the crowd more sensitively.

But mascots can be fractious. Their costumes are sweltering in August and April – it's like running in an oven – but they keep motivating the fans. Bertie Bee (Burnley) rugby tackled a streaker during a match against Preston North End, and Wolfie the Wolf (Wolves) fought with Three Little Pigs (Bristol City) at Ashton Gate. Hercules the Lion (Aston Villa) was fired after grappling with Miss Aston Villa.

4 **CAN** you name the football clubs associated with these three mascots – Gilbert the Gull, Chaddy the Owl and Whaddney the Robin? (3)

How does an artist design a football mascot's uniform? Well, first of all you could ask Partick Thistle's artist, a Turner Prize nominee who, in 2015, used his creative and satirical talent to construct an unusual mascot. Jaggy McBee, the previous Thistle mascot, had been consigned to a 'mascot place in the sky'. The new mascot, Kingsley, had empty eyes, a sun-like skull and crooked teeth. He was scary, funny and somewhat demonic. But there was a mixed reaction to Kingsley and some were still fond of Kingsley's predecessors, such as Jaggy McBee and Pee Tee the toucan.

5 **WHICH** artist was nominated for a Turner Prize before he designed the costume for a new Partick Thistle mascot called Kingsley?

On the last day of the 1988–89 season, Crystal Palace and Birmingham City fans arrived at the Selhurst Park ground in fancy dress costumes. When Palace scored, in the 12th minute, Birmingham fans invaded the pitch and it was like hundreds of mascots had arrived. Four sprinting nuns, a pantomime horse and a uniformed sailor ran across the centre circle. Adolf Hitler was attacked by Palace fans, and a boy was chased by Spiderman. The front end of a cow was carried off the pitch on one stretcher and the cow's rear end was on another. White Rabbit was in trouble by a corner flag, five gorillas chanted 'City, City, City' and one fan climbed to the top of a floodlight pylon. Crystal Palace won 4-1. Palace were chasing promotion to the top flight and Birmingham were certain to be relegated.

6 **HOW** many were arrested? (Two either way.)

The first annual Mascot Grand National race saw mascots turn out *en masse*. The race became a tradition in the 21st century, and actual racecourses, such as Huntingdon or Kempton Park, were used, with low barriers. But an increase in private company mascots caused a schism and one year the event was boycotted. Some football mascots felt it was better to take part in local events rather than national ones.

7 **WHICH** football clubs were associated with Harry the Hornet, Captain Gas and Scunny Bunny. (3)

In the 1930s one mascot dressed like Charlie Chaplin and did tricks with a bowler hat. Old-time football mascots used to be a cross between cheerleaders and confection-sellers. The Everton mascot, dressed in blue and white club colours, threw Dobson's sweets into the crowd. Another man sold mints. In the 1940s and 1950s a self-appointed mascot turned up at Liverpool's Anfield ground with his togs underneath his best suit, and then he'd strip off and dribble the ball along the touchline before the game started. In the 1960s a Derby County man came on the pitch at half time and did laps of the field. These fans were all mascots in their own minds.

8 Rick Minter wrote a book called *Mascots*, published in 2004. The book's sub-title has three words beginning with 'F'. **WHAT** are they? No swearing is involved! (3)

At big matches, a number of rituals may take place – presentations to dignitaries, a minute's tribute, anthems, photographs – and the teams take up suitable positions. Steve Perryman, the official guest at the 2005 FA Vase Final, found he had to meet 22 players, 22 mascots, ten substitutes and a group of club officials. Mascots and players can also clash colours with spectators or stewards. The Queen's Park Rangers' mascot was despatched for confusing the referee in the game against Preston, and Norwich City players complained that Lofty the Lion looked like a Bolton Wanderers player. At top-class stadia, kit can clash with thousands of replica shirts.

9 In April 1996 the grey shirts clashed with Sir Alex Ferguson when Manchester United went 3-0 down before half time. **WHAT** colour shirts were used by United in the second half?

The word 'mascot' comes from the French *mascotte*, meaning a lucky charm. The word was popularised by a comic opera called *La Mascotte* in December 1880. The opera is about a farm girl called Bettina who brings good luck to whoever possesses her as long as she remains a virgin. Mascots for football tournaments have included World Cup Willie, Tip & Tap, and Juanito.

10 **WHAT** was the name of England's lion mascot for the 1996 UEFA European Championships?

THE ANSWERS 135

3

OUTLANDISH SCORELINES

There was a feast of goals on Christmas Day and Boxing Day in 1935 when Oldham Athletic and Tranmere Rovers played each other home and away. Oldham Athletic beat Tranmere Rovers 4-1 in the first match and scored four again in the return … but Oldham lost 13-4 in the second match. It was a singular scoreline which would have been rare in local football, let alone a professional Division Three (North) match. Tranmere's Robert 'Bunny' Bell scored nine of the team's 13. Harold Bell was only 16 when he scored a hat-trick in Tranmere's 6-4 victory over Bradford Park Avenue at the start of the Second World War, and he went on to play a high number of consecutive appearances (including matches in the FA Cup, Liverpool Senior Cup and Cheshire Bowl).

1 How many consecutive appearances did Harold Bell make? **WAS IT** 167, 244, 336, 401 or 459?

At some point in a season fans might see an avalanche of goals in their favour, while other fans are starved of goals. Consider the case of Stirling Albion. In 1981 Albion went 1,293 minutes without scoring. The bad run started just before they lost 3-0 to Celtic in the fourth round of the Scottish FA Cup on 31 January 1981 and ended just after they'd lost 3-0 to Motherwell on 2 May 1981, the last match of the season. The 14 full matches without a goal included four 0-0 draws, seven 1-0 defeats, one 2-0 defeat and two 3-0 defeats.

2 **WHICH** is the only team beginning with the letter 'T' to have won the Scottish Cup?

In September 1885 Arbroath beat Bon Accord 36-0 in a Scottish Cup tie. It was claimed that the Arbroath goalkeeper didn't touch the ball during the match. Instead, the goalkeeper spent time keeping warm and sheltering under a spectator's umbrella. 'The leather was landed between the posts 41 times, but five of the times were disallowed,' reported the *Scottish Athletic Journal*. 'Here and there, enthusiasts would be seen, scoring sheet and pencil in hand, taking note of the goals as one would score runs at a cricket match.' Eighteen-year-old John 'Jock' Petrie was credited with 13 Arbroath goals in that 1885 match.

3 **WHICH** two teams from the Scottish Premier League played out a 6-6 draw during the 2009–10 season?

Jean Kaltack scored 16 goals when Vanuatu beat Micronesia 46-0 in the 2015 Olympic qualifying tournament. Micronesia's other defeats were to Tahiti (30-0) and Fiji (38-0). In 2001 the magic number of 13 appeared again when Australia's Archie Thompson notched 13 in a 2002 World Cup qualifier against American Samoa.

4 **HOW** many did Australia score against American Samoa in that 2001 World Cup qualifier? (Two points for exact answer, one point for three goals either way.)

On 14 November 1959, Villa Park, Birmingham, was the venue for an unusual match. An 11-goal win coincided with Aston Villa's 11th victory of the season, and, unsurprisingly, it was achieved by 11 Villa footballers. The opposition, Charlton Athletic, used three goalkeepers during the match. Charlton goalkeeper Willie Duff was injured and had to play out of goal (in the days before substitutes were allowed). The score was 1-1 after 22 minutes but Villa were in double figures by the 72nd minute. It was a gloomy afternoon and the reporters worked hard to distinguish the players.

5 An England international scored five for Villa that day, and he would become the first player to be picked for an England team while playing abroad (in Italy). **WHO** was he?

In March 2001 Willenhall Town Women beat Burton Brewers Women 57-0 at Noose Lane in the Division One North of the West Midlands Women's League. That meant Burton Brewers had conceded 234 goals and scored three in the first seven months of the season. But even some higher-class fixtures can provide high scores. In 2009 Thailand women beat Malaysia women 14-0 in the Sea Games and nine different players scored goals. In 2010 Keynsham Town Ladies beat Somerset and Langton Ladies by 41 goals. The most dramatic match came in October 2002, when AS Adema beat SO Emyrne (SOE) 149-0 in a national championship. SOE protested a refereeing decision – a disputed penalty in a previous match – by repeatedly scoring own goals.

6 AS Adema and SO Emyrne were from **WHICH** country?

Two women's teams were totally mismatched when they played a game in the Second Division of the Portuguese Women's League. Benfica beat Ponte de Frielas 28-0 after leading 16-0 at half time. Some top Portuguese women international footballers were in a lower division, whereas some newcomers to the game were finding their way. There was even a mismatch of kit. The Benfica team had red shirts, white shorts and red socks whereas Ponte de Frielas wore white shirts, red shorts and white socks. The referee wore a bright yellow shirt but a number of possible offsides weren't noted by the assistants.

7 Benfica manager Béla Guttmann put a curse on the club in 1962. **HOW** many of their eight European finals since 1962 have Benfica won?

Wilfred Minter was particularly known for one match – an FA Cup replay between St Albans and Dulwich Hamlet in November 1922, when he scored all seven goals for St Albans City, but his team lost 8-7. The following Saturday Minter was made Dulwich Hamlet captain and the band played when he went to toss the coin. Minter's overall career was even more striking. He scored 356 goals in 362 league matches, 57 goals in 37 for the Hertfordshire County XI and 72 goals in 67 friendly matches. Overall that meant 485 goals in 466 matches.

8 **WHAT** did the crowd sing?

Six matches between a Football League XI and an All British XI were played during the Second World War. These fixtures brought 45 goals. The matches were played in Lancashire, Yorkshire and Staffordshire. One of the matches, played in April 1941, saw a Football League XI beat a British XI 9-7 at Anfield, Liverpool. These were two All Star teams – more than half were internationals and nine had played in FA Cup Finals – but clearly defences were not on top. At half time the League XI led 3-2, but the second half brought 11 more goals. Wags suggested that the cricket season had come a month early.

9 **WHICH** Football League club played at Anfield from 1888 to 92?

In July 2018 Everton beat the Austrian team ATV Irdning 22-0 in a warm-up friendly. Everton's opponents, a fifth-level team, were outclassed, outplayed and outscored. The stunning backcloth of Alpine mountains didn't distract Everton players from their task of scoring as many as possible. It was 10-0 at half time and then the new manager, Marco Silva, made ten substitutions and raised the scoring pace. Kevin Mirallas came on and scored four in the next seven minutes (five in all) and hat-tricks were scored by Cenk Tosun, Ademola Lookman and Oumar Niasse. It was a good start for new Everton manager Marco Silva.

10 **WHAT** was odd about Manchester City's numbering in the 1933 FA Cup Final against Everton?

THE ANSWERS 136

4

LONG-RUNNING SAGAS

In the 1954–55 season, Stoke City and Bury played a total of 562 minutes (nine hours and 22 minutes) at five different venues. This created an FA Cup record at the time. The teams drew 1-1 at Bury and were 1-1 in the replay at Stoke when a snowstorm forced the game to be abandoned after 112 minutes. Thereafter matches were played at Goodison Park, Everton, where the teams drew 3-3 (after extra time), Anfield, Liverpool, where the match finished 2-2 (after extra time) and, finally, at Old Trafford, where the match went to extra time again. Each game meant more gate receipts but took its toll on the players.

1 The tie was played on five grounds – Gigg Lane, Victoria Ground, Goodison Park, Anfield and Old Trafford. **WHICH** ground attracted the highest attendance?

One round later, again in the 1954–55 season, Doncaster Rovers, a lowly second-tier club, played Aston Villa, an upper-first-tier club. This went to five FA Cup matches in 18 days. The Rovers drew 0-0 at home to Aston Villa, 2-2 at Villa Park (after extra time),

1-1 at Maine Road, Manchester (after extra time), 0-0 at Hillsborough (abandoned after 90 minutes) and then Doncaster won 3-1 at The Hawthorns. The two teams played for 510 minutes.

2 The tie was played on five grounds – Belle Vue, Villa Park, Maine Road, Hillsborough and the Hawthorns. **WHICH** ground attracted the highest attendance?

Alvechurch and Oxford City took six games and 660 playing minutes to settle an FA Cup tie in November 1971. 'We didn't know the Oxford players at the start,' recalled an Alvechurch player, 'but we were on first-name terms at the end. We were turning up as if long-lost mates. It was almost like going to work every day – the same teams, the same players and the same result. Tactics went out of the window. We didn't change anything. We just carried on playing the same way. Before every game, Rhys Davies, the manager, used to say, "Go out and give it some tonk and bottle." Eventually the crowd sang "Keep Right on to the End of the Road" and "Auld Lang Syne".' Such a close association was formed that it was difficult to work out who was in which team.

3 **WHO** managed Kidderminster Harriers for nearly 16 years (1983–98) and during that time knocked Birmingham City and Preston North End out of the FA Cup?

The pitfalls of drawn-out fixtures were evident. Some players were exhausted at the end of the tie, and spectators never knew when they'd be home for their tea. Experiments with golden goals (1993–2004) and silver goals (1998–2004) seemed too difficult to manage and FIFA resorted to the drama of kicks from the penalty mark. In the Euro semi-final 2004, when the silver goal was still being used, Traianos Dellas (Greece) scored the winner on the stroke of half time in extra time and the match ended too abruptly.

4 In the 1992 UEFA Championship Yugoslavia were disqualified because their country was in the grip of break-up and warfare: **(A) WHICH** country replaced Yugoslavia; and **(B) WHICH** team won the tournament?

Dixie Dean was lauded for the 60 League goals he scored in the 1927–28 season, but in fact he scored 100. They came from various sources: League goals (60), Continental tour with the English FA (nine), Inter-League matches (six), against Blackpool in the Hospital Cup (five), an FA trial match at Middlesbrough (five), the Fleetwood Disaster Fund match (four), an FA trial match against West Brom (three), an Everton tour (three), FA Cup ties (three) and an FA tour (two). Dean's achievement is probably unsurpassable.

5 Dixie Dean had a near namesake who scored six goals for Celtic in a League game and two Scottish Cup Final hat-tricks in the 1970s. **HOW** do you spell the more recent player's name?

It was called the Big Freeze. The cold and icy weather started just before Christmas 1962 and only three of the 32 Cup ties were played on 5 January. Fifteen ties had ten or more postponements, and Bolton Wanderers went 69 days – early December to mid-February – without playing a match. It was reminiscent of the winter of 1946–47, when the season ended in the middle of June. A pools panel was set up in 1963. The panellists decided on the results.

6 The panel consisted of a former Arsenal manager, the Preston plumber, a former captain of Rangers and Scotland, a referee who hosted *It's a Knock-out* and an England international. **CAN** you name any of them? (5)

On 22 April 1964 the reading of the classified results brought up a classic tongue-twister – Forfar 5, East Fife 4. But that season Forfar Athletic had also lost 6-4 at home to Morton and 8-2 at home to Montrose, finishing second from bottom. In October 2011 there was a close approximation with the score East Fife 4, Forfar 3. Yet another interesting result came in July 2018 when East Fife drew 1-1 with Forfar Athletic in a Group B Scottish League Cup match which went to kicks from the penalty mark. Nine out of ten kicks were converted from the penalty spot. Hence the shoot-out victory from 12 yards out – Forfar 5, East Fife 4.

7 **WHICH** famous comedian, president of Luton Town, popularised the tongue-twister result Forfar 5, East Fife 4?

The longest ever Cup tie came in a qualifying round of the 1980–81 FA Trophy competition when Bridlington Trinity (North Yorkshire) were drawn against Netherfield (Cumbria). The tie went to seven matches with over 13½ hours of football. It included six draws (one 0-0 draw, three 1-1 draws and two 2-2 draws) before Netherfield won the seventh match 2-0. The four venues were Netherfield, Bridlington Trinity, Goole and Chorley. The players and the two clubs suffered under the strain. There is something to be said for kicks from the penalty mark.

8 **HOW** many FA Trophy matches did Netherfield play to get to the second round?

In the icy winter of 1979 Inverness Thistle played Falkirk in a Scottish Cup second round tie. Well, they should have played each other. In fact the tie at the Kings Mill ground was postponed 29 times. The run of postponements continued for 47 days, from 6 January to when the match was played on 22 February. Inverness and Falkirk were lucky. Airdrie and Stranraer had 33 postponements.

9 The Big Freeze was a time for quiz questions: **WHICH** English League club's name has 11 letters with no repeats?

In November 1899 Sheffield Wednesday's home game with Aston Villa was abandoned after 79 minutes and the remaining 11 minutes played 15 weeks later. Wednesday added another goal to win 4-1. But the procedure has been used more recently in other countries. In May 1989 Real Madrid and Osasuna played the remaining 47 minutes of their match three months after the first attempt had been abandoned. Osasuna scored in February, and Real Madrid equalised in May. The 1995 Spanish Cup Final was abandoned after 79 minutes when a storm broke out. Valencia and Deportivo La Coruña returned to the stadium two days later to play the remaining 11 minutes.

10 Can you give five reasons **WHY** the Nottingham Forest v Spurs match, in February 1996, was abandoned after 14 minutes? (5)

THE ANSWERS 137

5

SINGING AND CHANTING

In the 1940s and 1950s FA Cup Finals brought traditional songs to an audience of 100,000 at Wembley Stadium. The songs ranged from Welsh hymns such as 'Land of My Fathers', war songs like 'John Brown's Body' and miners' songs such as 'Clementine'. Cup Final songs were conducted by a bandleader, Arthur Caiger, who led the community singing and moved the spectators to tears because so many people felt lucky to be alive.

1 **WHICH** famous hymn has been sung at every FA Cup Final since 1927?

There had always been club-oriented chants and songs, such as the Pompey Chimes and West Ham United's anthem 'I'm forever blowing bubbles'. In the 1920s Celtic fans sang 'Hail Glorious St Patrick' and Rangers fans sang 'Boyne Waters'. Spectators became more vociferous in the 1950s. The noise was still mainly cheering, clapping and feet-stamping, as well as 'oohs' and 'aahs' or a shout for 'Corner' or 'Handball'. In 1961 Tottenham Hotspur won the Cup and League double and their fans enjoyed the music of 'Glory, glory, hallelujah' from 'John Brown's Body'. In the 1960s the singing at football matches became more orchestrated.

2 The Tottenham Hotspur captain during the 1950s and early 1960s had previously played with Barnsley and Aston Villa. He was a great talker but in one Shredded Wheat advert all he said was five words: 'Pass the hot milk, please.' **WHO** was he?

The world of musicology includes many football songs. Talent is brought in to help rehearse footballers' songs, especially when a major tournament is happening. Musical pieces include the England World Cup Squad's 'Back Home' (1970), Chelsea FC's 'Blue is the Colour' (1972), Rod Stewart's 'Ola Ola' (1978), New Order's 'World in Motion' (1990), Baddiel and Skinner's 'Three Lions' (1996), Fat Les's 'Vindaloo' (1998), Ant and Dec's 'We're on the Ball' (2002), and the Colne Valley Male Voice Choir's 'Our Boys, Our Heroes' (2006).

3 Kirsty MacColl's 1999 song was more about a relationship on the edge than a football team on the brink, but the two can go together. **WHAT** was it called?

The song 'Nice One, Cyril' started its journey in a 1972 Wonderloaf Bread TV advertising campaign. The football song was released in February 1973, a month before Tottenham Hotspur met Norwich City in the League Cup Final. The artists were Cockerel Chorus (Harold Spiro and Helen Clarke) and the song was taken up with great gusto by Spurs fans idolising Cyril the full-back. The song rose to 14th in the hit parade. Sadly, the full-back died when he was 47, when his football management career was taking off.

4 **WHAT** was the surname of the Spurs man lauded in the song 'Nice one, Cyril'?

World Cup years are particularly inviting for football music. In 1978 Nottingham Forest FC and a Nottingham group recorded their version of 'We've Got the Whole World in our Hands'. The Forest players put together a rehearsal on the team coach after a training session. The song, originally a gospel song from the 1920s, had been recorded in the 1950s by Laurie London, before the 1978 Nottingham Forest rendition. The website www.fanchants.com has compiled over 25,000 football songs.

5 The group accompanying Nottingham Forest players once recorded a song called 'Billy Don't Be a Hero'. **WHAT** was the group's name?

Michael Marra wrote the song 'Hamish the Goalie' as a tribute to a Dundee United goalkeeper who scored three penalty kicks in 477 appearances. Marra's widow Peggy said: 'He loved going to places like Forfar where you are so close you can hear what the players are saying, what the ref is saying, and the manager comes and has a wee lean at the side and talks to the fans.' After one of Hamish's spot-kicks hit the post, a few Dundee United colleagues surrounded the opposing goalie while Hamish sprinted back to his own penalty area. Dundee United's heyday was between 1959 and 1993, and the club had only two managers during that period, Jerry Kerr (1959–71) and Jim McLean (1971–93).

6 In 1966–67 Kerr's team played their first UEFA Cup match, beating a big Spanish club. **WHICH** club was it?

Spontaneous chanting and singing may (or may not) have originated at Anfield, Liverpool. On one occasion in 1963 a trainer brought an injured player to his feet only for the player to collapse over the trainer. The Anfield crowd hardly missed a beat and sang, 'He loves you, yeah, yeah, yeah.' And chanting was used to send messages to Nottingham Forest players – 'Give it to Moore, give it to Moore, he will score …' A school playground chant ('Eee-aye-addio, the farmer wants a wife') was launched nationally by Liverpool fans at the 1965 FA Cup Final ('Eee-aye-addio, we've scored a goal'). On a foggy February night at Anfield in 1968 Liverpool scored a goal at the Anfield Road end and the Kop chanted 'Who scored that goal?' The Anfield Road end replied with 'Tony Hateley' and the Kop sang 'Thank you very much' to the tune of a Scaffold song.

7 The Moore in question had a double-barrelled surname. **WHAT** was his full name, hyphen and all?

Nigel Tattersfield, who worked with Desmond Morris on *The Soccer Tribe*, found that conversational chanting took off in the 1960s when youth gangs took over ends of football grounds. 'Travel to grounds became easier,' said Tattersfield, 'boys went by themselves rather than with their fathers, and groups of fans regularly confronted each other.' By the late 1970s there was ritual interaction between rival fans – taunts about the score, pleas for noise and atmosphere, and threats of what was going to happen later. 'You'll never walk alone' became 'You'll never walk again'. Tattersfield distinguished several forms of football chanting, including solidarity chants ('We are United'), game-directed chants ('Attack, attack'), chants aimed at fickle supporters ('Half-time supporters'), boredom-inducing chants ('We've got the ball') and identity-establishing chants ('Can you hear us, Liverpool?').

8 **WHAT** is the oldest football song still being sung by a club's fans? First composed in the 1890s, it starts with 'Kick it off, throw it in, have a little scrimmage.'

When Oxford United played Derby County in the late 1980s, Kevin Maxwell was chairman of Oxford United and his father, Robert Maxwell, was chairman of Derby County. Robert Maxwell had previously been chairman at Oxford United and it was assumed that he still called the shots at Oxford, as seen by the sale of Dean Saunders from Oxford United to Derby County in 1988. When Derby County played at Oxford the next season the away fans sang, 'We hate Maxwell more than you do' and Oxford fans replied by singing, 'We hate Maxwell more than you do'. Then supporters of both clubs sang, 'If you all hate Maxwell clap your hands.'

9 **WHAT** name did Robert Maxwell give to the Football League management committee?

The song 'Careless Hands', first recorded in 1948, reached number six in the UK singles charts in 1967. In December Leeds United played Liverpool. During the game Leeds goalkeeper Gary Sprake planned to throw the ball out to a colleague and stopped because he saw a Liverpool player running towards him … but when Sprake tried to retain the ball it slipped out of his hand and went into the net. At half time the Liverpool announcer played 'Careless Hands' and the Kop sang it through the second half.

10 **WHO** sang the 1967 English version of 'Careless Hands'? The singer was briefly on the books of Northampton Town.

THE ANSWERS ☞ 138

6

THE JOKERS

In October 2011 Manchester United lost 6-1 to Manchester City at Old Trafford. Three City goals came in stoppage time and, within minutes, jokes were circulating. What about the special helpline for Manchester United fans? Just dial 0161-616161. In the final match of the season Manchester United looked certain to be League Champions. City needed a win but were 2-1 down to Queen's Park Rangers. Then City scored two in added time. Manchester City had a better goal difference that season, but only because they had won 6-1 at Manchester United. Had that been a 2-1 win rather than 6-1 the two Manchester clubs would have had identical statistics and the title decided by a play-off at a neutral ground.

1 **WHICH** one-cap international, sent off in the final game of 2011–12, titled his autobiography *No Nonsense* for the English edition and *Sweet and Tender Hooligan* for the French? Born in Liverpool, he went into league management in 2018.

On paper the two-legged League Cup was a good idea. The competition gave spectators the opportunity of watching big clubs. However, in some cases, the two-legged ties were virtually over after the first leg. In 1983–84, Derby County lost 3-0 at home against Birmingham City in the first leg and were trailing 4-0 in the second leg (7-0 on aggregate). Someone near the front of the stand shouted, 'Turn the lights out, let's all go home.' Then someone from the back of the stand shouted back: 'Leave the lights on, I'm reading.'

2 Harry Zussman once said, 'You wait all week for the match to begin, and then, when it starts, you can't wait for it to end.' Zussman was chairman of a club promoted to the top tier in 1962 (with Liverpool) for one season. **WHICH** club was it?

There were still wisecracks from the stand, such as 'Get off the field, let grass grow' or 'You're about as much use as a chocolate teapot'. One player completely missed his kick. 'Here's your leg back, Mister,' shouted a fan behind the goal. In 1979 a female referee, Pat Dunn, gave the kiss of life to a player in a local match. Soon afterwards she came out to referee a match between two men's teams and all 22 players were lying on the floor demanding to be given the kiss of life. In May 1976 Dunn became the first woman to referee a competitive men's fixture in England (in the Dorset County Sunday League).

3 In the 1995–96 season **WHO** was the first woman to be an assistant referee for a Premier League match?

Newspaper sub-editors have fun with headlines. In February 2011, when Grimsby Town lost 3-0 at Fleetwood Town in the old Conference, a Grimsby forum, *The Fishy*, ran a fine headline (COD BATTERS HADDOCK AT THEIR PLAICE). Other spectacular headlines include one from *The Sun* in 2000 after

Celtic had hosted Inverness Caledonian Thistle (SUPER CALEY GO BALLISTIC, CELTIC ARE ATROCIOUS). At one time the head of Ruskin College, Oxford, faced a college rebellion and, around the same time, Oxford United FC striker Dean Saunders was in great form when playing against Manchester United (OXFORD DEAN EXPELS REDS). A clever headline was inevitable when Scotsman Gerry Queen played for Crystal Palace and the match became a little feisty (QUEEN IN BRAWL AT THE PALACE).

4 **WHICH** one of these teams has never reached the World Cup Finals? Cuba, Dutch East Indies, Palestine, Zaire?

Ralph McTell, the musician, singer and football fan, once watched an injured player receiving treatment in the 1960s. The Craven Cottage ground was quiet until McTell heard a voice from the crowd: 'Don't just stand there, Fulham, practise.' On another occasion the coach of an under-13 match was at the touchline geeing up his young charges. His schoolboy team was top of the league and unbeaten, but they were losing 1-0 at half time. So their manager set into them during the half-time interval. 'You can do much better than this,' he said. 'You're playing like a bunch of schoolboys.' Which they were.

5 Fulham had two loyal England internationals during the post-war period. One won 56 England caps (22 as England captain) and the other won 37 caps and a World Cup winners' medal. **WHO** were they? (2)

Chesterfield were at home to Wrexham one day and the ball was slowly dribbling towards the net. It was about a foot from the goal line – goalkeeper and defenders nowhere in sight – when a Wrexham player tried to help it home, but instead he put his foot on the top of the ball and it squirmed out behind him. A Chesterfield fan shouted, 'We'll have him next season.' One of the biggest events in Chesterfield FC's history was their 1996–97 FA Cup run to a semi-final replay. Chesterfield were a third-tier team when they reached the last four and forced a replay.

6 **WHICH** England World Cup winner started his career at Chesterfield?

One day in the 1960s a team's captain went down injured. The diagnosis seemed to be concussion – the captain was seeing stars and feeling dizzy. The trainer asked the usual questions: 'Where are you? What's the score?' 'I'm at Wembley,' the player replied. 'We're 2-0 up against Brazil and I've got them both.'

7 **WHICH** three countries have overall positive records against Brazil? (3)

There was a point in the new century, around 2011, when a Liverpool fan suggested that the Anfield club should sign three new players: Gary Neville, the veteran Manchester United full-back; John Wark, the experienced Ipswich player who might be available on loan; and Jason Euell, who played for Wimbledon and Charlton Athletic. That was Euell, Neville, Wark on loan.

8 **PLACE** the three players – Euell, Neville and Wark – in order of **(A)** League appearances, and **(B)** appearances for their national teams.

Brian Fidler was an outrageous showman who played for Heanor Town, Macclesfield and Burton Albion in the 1960s and 1970s. After scoring one goal, during a Cheshire League match, Fidler taunted Altrincham officials until Altrincham manager Freddie Pye responded by throwing a bucketful of water at him. After scoring for Macclesfield in the 1970 FA Trophy Final, Fidler lapped Wembley before jumping the fence and hugging fans.

9 England's three goalkeepers at the 1958 World Cup Finals came from Burnley, Bolton and Sheffield United and had 11 caps between them. **WHO** were they? (3)

Kids and their jokes, eh? These are suitable for fans aged five to eight: What part of a football pitch smells the nicest? The Scenter Spot. How do footballers stay cool? They stand near the fans. What do you call a woman who stands behind the goal line and stops the ball from running away? Annette.

10 **HOW** did the football pitch end up as a triangle?

THE ANSWERS 139

7

FLOODLIGHTS

Experiments with floodlit football began in the 1870s. The main issues over the years have been ensuring a visible ball and the fears of floodlight failure. In the pioneering days, players and referees commented about dark patches on pitches, shadows and blind spots. The white ball came into official use in 1953 and Wolves wore fluorescent shirts in a 1954 friendly against Honvéd (Hungary). Evening kick-offs were only possible during August and April, and Saturday matches started at 2.15pm or 2.30pm during winter months. Over the years kick-offs have gone forward about half an hour and half-time intervals have gone from 10–15 minutes.

1. In 1950, **WHICH** southern ground in England was the first to have floodlights installed permanently?

In August 2017 St Helen's Town (Lancashire) played their first match at Ruskin Drive. The score was 0-0 when opponents Abbey Hulton United won a penalty for handball in the 95th minute. United's Josh Graham put the ball on the spot and considered how he would score. He was starting his run-up when the lights went out. Apparently there was a 10pm curfew on the floodlights. Earlier that evening heavy traffic on the M6 motorway had delayed the kick-off by 26 minutes. Abbey Hulton's manager David Riley couldn't see where the dugout was. The final score was registered as 0-0 and Graham never had his chance to win the game.

2 In the 2018–19 National League **WHICH** three clubs have an 'e' at the end of their names?

Football clubs have faced power cuts, equipment failure and sabotage. In the mid-1960s it became commonplace for clubs to have a standby generator system, especially during periods of industrial action. A match between Southampton and Leeds United in December 1960 lasted 158 minutes because the floodlights failed twice. A crowd of 13,000 people waited patiently for an hour in freezing conditions for a 1985 match between Queen's Park Rangers and Nottingham Forest, but electrical engineers were unable to restore power to two pylons.

3 **WHICH** team changed their shirt colours from royal blue to all-white in 1961?

There was a controversial FA Buildbase Vase match in January 2017 when South Shields were at home to Morpeth Town in the last 32. A home player was sent off for a second caution in stoppage time of the first half. South Shields went 2-1 up and Morpeth equalised. Then Morpeth scored twice more and went 4-2 ahead. Then the lights started flickering and the arena went dark. The match was replayed at Morpeth's home ground. South Shields beat Morpeth Town 4-0 and went on to win the trophy.

4 **WHAT** is the connection between Morpeth Town FC, Kris Kristofferson, Waylon Jennings, Willie Nelson and Johnny Cash?

Let there be light. An old joke suggests that when the floodlights go out everybody should raise their hands (because many hands make light work). Another floodlight failure came in a South West derby between Exeter City and Plymouth Argyle, but the fans reached for their mobile phones, pressed the light mechanism and sang Bob Marley's 'Don't worry about a thing'. A similar power cut happened at Sunderland's Stadium of Light, which was briefly referred to as Sunderland's 'Stadium of Darkness'. And when Arsenal beat Coventry City 4-0 in an FA Cup fifth round tie some of the lights went out towards half time. Thousands of smart phones were waved around the Emirates Stadium, the match continued until half time, and the problem was fixed during the interval.

5 **WHICH** international team did Bob Marley support?

The first competitive match at Derby County's Pride Park Stadium, in 1997, was a singular occasion. The crowd was 24,571 and the opponents were Wimbledon, but the floodlights failed after 56 minutes with Derby County 2-1 up. Ashley Ward, who had scored the last goal at the old Baseball Ground, thought he had also scored the first goal at Pride Park, but goals in abandoned matches didn't count. By the time the lights were back on, 34 minutes later, the referee had abandoned the match.

6 **WHICH** player scored the first goal at Pride Park that actually counted?

There has been lots of uncertainty regarding floodlights. In 2015 one club in the National League South was playing a floodlit match against Hemel Hempstead Town when three floodlights broke down moments before half time. In another match Fleet Town were 4-0 down to Petersfield Town when the match was abandoned. There have been cases of floodlights failing during penalty shootouts.

7 **WHICH** team played at Treyew Road, near to one of the two three-spire cathedrals in England?

In October 1996 Estonia were scheduled to play Scotland in Tallinn. The match had a 6.45pm kick-off, but there were complaints from the Scots about the standard of the Tallinn floodlights. FIFA switched the kick-off time to 3pm (with only a few hours' notice). Estonia complained because this new arrangement played havoc with security arrangements, television contracts, the players' preparation and ticket-holders' ability to attend (especially if they were at work during the day). When 3pm arrived, Scotland's players were the only ones on the pitch. The referee started the game and abandoned it after the first kick.

8 **WHICH** neutral venue was used for Scotland v Estonia on 11 February 1997? The venue was one where Glenn Hoddle spent four years (1987–91) and Arsène Wenger seven years (1987–94)

A spate of floodlight failures in the late 1990s eventually led to four men being jailed for blacking out floodlit football games for a betting coup. The criminals were caught tampering with lights during a Charlton Athletic–Liverpool match. When the referee terminated a match between West Ham and Crystal Palace, he was asked by police to delay the announcement so that transport arrangements could be brought forward. Some years later, during the 2005 League Cup semi-final, the floodlights went out. When the lights came back on Jimmy Bullard (Wigan) was standing with the ball on the Arsenal goal line, poised to put the ball in the net. Everyone had a good laugh about that.

9 **WHICH** was the first professional club Jimmy Bullard played for?

Floodlights are superb when they work, but it may cost £10,000–20,000 for clubs to overhaul their systems. Floodlights can also sway dangerously, and lights can pop. When Aldershot hosted Southend United, in December 2011, the match was abandoned at half time when the lights failed. 'It was in the lap of the gods,' said Southend manager Paul Sturrock, whose team led 1-0 with Aldershot down to ten men. 'We can take encouragement from what we did. If we can take that into the next game, I will be very happy.'

10 **WHICH** team won the rearranged match?

THE ANSWERS 140

8

PROFESSIONAL FOOTBALL

John Boileau applied for the job as Middlesbrough manager because he'd had great success while he was manager of Doncaster Rovers and Rushden & Diamonds (once backed by Dr Marten's shoes). He had overseen Thierry Henry, Fernando Torres, Raul and Zinedine Zidane. Unfortunately Boileau's success was all with Football Manager 2005.

1 **WHAT** links Dodgin, Clough, Bond and Johnson?

Footballers spend a lot of time hanging about. They frequent hotel rooms and stadiums, waiting for the match to start, preparing for the match, fearing losing, and being in situations where most of us would get bored. But footballers can also create something out of nothing. They design pranks, offer wisecracks, crack jokes and experience camaraderie. Eventually they have a lifestyle which is punctuated with occasional units of intense concentration, such as playing matches. The football world is an arena of excitement and uncertainty.

2 Kevin Curry, playing for D & R Motors in the Midlands Regional Alliance, scored from the kick-off

against Melbourne Dynamo in February 1999. Curry's wind-assisted shot went into the net in an estimated 1.5 seconds. **IS THIS** possible?

When Wimbledon played Newcastle United in February 1988 Vinnie Jones followed Paul Gascoigne wherever the Newcastle player went. Jones tackled and taunted Gazza all afternoon. At one point, while waiting for a free kick to be taken, Jones reached behind and grabbed Gazza's testicles, a scene captured and immortalised by a classic photograph by Monte Fresco. After the match a Newcastle fan presented Gascoigne with a bunch of roses. Gazza then gave someone a rose to take to Vinnie Jones.

3 **HOW** did Vinnie Jones respond to Gazza's present?

Brian Gearing's study of footballers' retirement showed that professional players have careers that end early, and they have to reinvent themselves later in life. The average length of a football career was about eight years. Professional players focused on the build-up to the match, the participation, and the anti-climax after the final whistle. Footballers have well-defined measures of success and an unusual relationship with the public. But nobody leaves a football career without injury. If the injury is career-threatening it may lead to an enforced career change. Football is a fantasy profession in an excitement arena.

4 **WHICH** Dutch international's record of scoring in ten successive post-war games was overtaken by Jamie Vardy?

Harold Wilson, MP for Ormskirk (1945–50) and Huyton (1950–83), was Prime Minister from 1964–70 and 1974–76. Wilson once spoke at length with Bill Shankly, the famous Liverpool manager. The two men agreed that they were not on the football field themselves, but they had important off-the-field jobs: they both chose the right people and delegated work. 'Not only that,' Wilson added. 'if your team gets relegated, as mine did in 1970, some people start saying that they want a change.'

5 **WHICH** football team did Harold Wilson support as a young boy?

Football has seen a forest of Sherwoods, and here are three of them. Tim Sherwood captained the team that won the 1994–95 Premier League. Alf Sherwood was a famous Wales full-back, the king of sliding tackles, who won 41 caps for Wales and captained Cardiff City from Division Three (South) to the top division. And goalkeeper Steve Sherwood made over 500 appearances for Watford and Grimsby Town in an 11-year period which saw Watford rise from the Fourth Division to runners-up in the top flight.

6 **WHEN** Watford and Everton came out for the 1984 FA Cup Final it was clear that both sides had the same theme tune. What was it?

When Jack Tinn joined Portsmouth as manager, in the summer of 1927, he took over a club that had risen from the Southern League to the top division in seven years. Tinn was fortunate that the Portsmouth area had survived the economic depression better than many football towns. He steered the club to the 1929 FA Cup Final but an injury to left-back Bell probably cost Pompey the game. Five years later Portsmouth lost 2-1 to Manchester City in their second FA Cup Final, partly because Allen's injury changed the game's destiny. And five more years passed before Portsmouth finally won the FA Cup by beating Wolverhampton Wanderers 4-1 in 1939. Portsmouth held the trophy for seven years.

7 In **WHICH** three places was the FA Cup trophy kept after Portsmouth had beaten Wolves 4-1 in 1939? **(A)** in the Football Association vault in London, **(B)** in the cellar of Jack Tinn's house, **(C)** in the cells of a police station, **(D)** in a local Hampshire bank, or **(E)** in an air raid shelter?

During the late 1970s and early 1980s, Bob Murphy was a well-known manager in North West England. He never drove a car, but he was tough and remarkably successful. When one of his players broke his nose Murphy checked the player's fitness by throwing a ball into the player's face. If a player had an upset stomach Murphy would suggest wearing a nappy. On the North West circuit Murphy managed Southport, Mossley, Stalybridge Celtic and Northwich Victoria. At his house Murphy kept hundreds of files on players and technical drawings on the wall. In the 1980–81 FA Cup, under Murphy, Mossley beat Crewe Alexandra in the first round and then lost 3-1 to Mansfield Town in the second round.

8 In 1980 Bob Murphy was voted the North West manager of the year. **WHO** was runner-up to Murphy?

Pitch-slope is not mentioned in the laws, but competitions may have a maximum-gradient rule. Oxford United's Manor Ground (1925–2001) had a 7ft (just over 2m) slope (goalmouth to goalmouth), Rotherham United's Millmoor was only slightly less steep, and Lye Meadow (Alvechurch) dropped 5ft (1.5m) from goal to goal. Other famous slopes are now defunct, because the club has moved (e.g. the Nest at Norwich), gone bankrupt (Peel Park at Accrington Stanley) or the ground has been levelled (Hibernian's Easter Road). The 8ft (2.4m) slope at the old Barnet Underhill Stadium was difficult to deal with because the pitch composition and the setting made levelling the pitch a real uphill task.

9 **WHAT** is the new Barnet ground called?

Is there a moment when a dream team comes into being? In 2014–15 Leicester City manager Nigel Pearson oversaw a team that climbed from bottom of the League to safety by winning seven of the last nine matches. At the start of the next season Leicester City's chances to win the Premier League Championship were 5,000–1. Then everything ran like a dream. Under a new manager, Claudio Ranieri, the team set off on a title chase. Ranieri, previously known at Chelsea as The Tinkerman, now became known as The Thinkerman, and Jamie Vardy scored in 11 successive Premier League matches.

10 During the 2015–16 season Claudio Ranieri had three assistant managers, including one with a famous literary surname who'd previously played over 500 matches for teams in the West Midlands and on the East Coast. **WHO** was this particular assistant?

THE ANSWERS ☞ 141

9

TRAVEL TALES

One way to collect enough football anecdotes to last a lifetime is to emulate Jeremy Boon, who cycled to all Bristol City's home and away matches during the 2003–04 season. Thirty-five-year-old Boon cycled to 46 League matches and three play-off fixtures. His outposts included Hartlepool United away on a December Saturday and Grimsby Town away the next Tuesday. Boon was 30 miles (48.3km) from Grimsby's Blundell Park when he stopped to check his mobile phone and found ten messages about the postponement. He had to travel to Grimsby again in the February. Boon estimated that he cycled over 7,000 miles (11,265km).

1 **WHAT** is the estimated distance to be travelled by Grimsby Town FC personnel during the 2018–19 League season? **(A)** 5,912, **(B)** 7,474, **(C)** 8,703, or **(D)** 9,622.

Similarly, Simon Hood spent the 2009–10 season pedalling to every York City match in the National Conference. His experience included a postponed match at Altrincham on Monday 28 December. He logged his distances at around 10,000 miles (16,000km) as the National Conference had a number of outpost clubs.

Boon and Hood's clubs, Bristol City and York City, reached play-off finals but failed to win promotion. Along the way the two men met fascinating people, dealt with bike breakdowns, fixed numerous punctures and collected plenty of anecdotes. Hood then wrote his book, *Bicycle Kicks*. 'Go on, get out there, do something,' Hood advised others. 'Just make sure you follow a better team.'

2 In January 2010, in the FA Cup third round, top-flight Stoke City beat York City of the National Conference. **WHICH** Stoke City player created the first two Stoke goals with his notorious long throw-ins?

When Liverpool played AC Milan in the 2005 Champions League Final it looked all over when the Reds were 3-0 down at half time. Then Liverpool staged a remarkable comeback and the score was 3-3 after an hour. Extra time was played, kicks from the penalty mark were taken and Liverpool won those 3-2. After the late kick-off to the match, and the slow trip to Istanbul, it wasn't until early morning that Liverpool fans arrived at the airport. One teenager sprinted out of Arrivals and a journalist shouted, 'Tell me what it was like in Istanbul.' 'I'd love to tell you, lah,' said the young man, 'but I've got me chemistry A-level in ten minutes.'

3 Liverpool play in red shirts and Everton play in blue shirts. **WHAT** colour are the wheelie bins on Merseyside?

Joe Smith was Reading manager for four years and Blackpool manager for over 22. During Smith's time at Blackpool his team won promotion to Division One and the 1953 FA Cup Final. In the famous 'Matthews Final', Blackpool came from 3-1 down to win 4-3, although Bolton finished the match with only nine fit players. Joe

Smith once confronted one of his inside-forwards and asked what time the player had gone to bed. 'I was in bed by ten,' said the player, and Smith retorted, 'Yes, but whose bed?' On another occasion Smith rounded up his players for a pre-match team talk. 'Don't hang about in the bath afterwards, lads,' said Smith. 'We're catching the 5.20 train.' And that was the end of his talk.

4 Stanley Matthews was born on 1 February 1915. **WHEN** Duncan Edwards played his first match for England, was Matthews **(A)** more than twice the age of Edwards, **(B)** almost exactly twice the age, or **(C)** less than twice the age of Matthews?

In Vienna, Austria, in 1952, Nat Lofthouse of Bolton Wanderers played for England against Austria. England took the lead twice with goals by Lofthouse, and Austria drew level twice. The score was 2-2 and 60,000 people were engrossed. Then Tom Finney passed to Lofthouse, who was in the clear but had a long way to run. When Austrian goalkeeper Musil came to narrow the angle Lofthouse shot past the goalkeeper, who accidentally kicked Lofthouse on the shin. The England player didn't see the best goal of his career because he was down on the ground. The England players carried Lofthouse off the field.

5 **WHAT** sobriquet was given to Nat Lofthouse after the 3-2 victory against Austria?

When Nat Lofthouse was on *This is Your Life*, in April 1993, Tom Finney told a story about an incident in 1960: 'We went to Grimsby, and after the game, when you played at Grimsby, you used to get a parcel of fish,' said Finney. 'On this particular occasion Nat and I played. I got a parcel of plaice, Nat got a parcel of cod. I remember Nat going back to the chap and saying, "What's this all about, Finney's got plaice and I've only got cod?" And the chap said, "Well, Finney's played a lot better than you did tonight."' The occasion was an evening testimonial match for the dependants of a Grimsby Town trainer, Billy Evans, who had died of lung cancer in his late thirties.

6 As of 2017, **WHICH** five footballers had been BBC Sports Personality of the Year? (5)

The closest Stoke City came to an FA Cup Final was in 1971, when they were leading 2-1 in added time against Arsenal in the Hillsborough semi-final. Then Arsenal took a corner and Mahoney (Stoke) handled the ball on the goal-line, even though the ball was possibly going wide. Peter Storey (Arsenal) converted the penalty and the Stoke fans were disconsolate. Two Stoke fans returned together and kept saying, 'Why?' every mile or two. 'Why? Why?' Stoke lost the replay 2-0.

7 Sunderland did it in 1979 and Villa did it in 1981. **WHO** did it in 1980?

It is said that Pelé scored 1,281 goals in his career. He also won three World Cup winner's medals for Brazil. On 4 June 1972, when Pelé was 31, he played for Santos at the Happy Valley Stadium, Hong Kong. 'We were 2-1 up at half time against Santos,' said one of Pelé's opponents, who hailed from County Durham. 'We were the better team before the break, but it was a different matter after half time. Pelé decided to score three fantastic goals in about 15 minutes. After 65 minutes he went off and that was it. We lost 4-2 but it was a great experience being on the same pitch as the world's best player.' That speaker played nearly 500 League games, winning two League Cups and one European Cup.

8 Pelé's opponent played in black and white stripes before playing for Forest. At **WHICH** club was he managing director from May 1983 and July 1991?

After the Second World War Charlton Athletic recruited players from South Africa, including goalkeeper Albert Uytenbogaardt from Cape Town Trams. John Hewie came from Arcadia Shepherds in October 1949 and played 495 League matches. He won 19 Scotland caps, started four games as a makeshift goalkeeper and wore every shirt number. Stuart Leary (376 Charlton appearances) and Sid O'Linn (187) were part of the South African intake. Two brothers, Eddie and Peter Firmani, had played for Clyde FC in Cape Town. One of them, Eddie, won three caps for Italy and managed ten clubs, mainly in North America.

9 **WHO** contested the Battle of Highbury, the Battle of Berne, the Battle of Santiago and the Battle of Stamford Bridge?

He played football for Wales, scoring 23 goals in 38 internationals. In 1955 he left Cardiff City for PSV Eindhoven, but was banned *sine die* by the Football League for revelations about illegal payments during his Sunderland spell. In August 1968, aged 44, he acted as a substitute fielder for Glamorgan in their Championship match against Nottinghamshire at Swansea.

10 **WHO** was he? His Christian name began with a 'T' and his surname is associated with the Model T.

THE ANSWERS ☞ 142

10

THE LAWS OF ASSOCIATION FOOTBALL

The classic annual *The Laws of Association Football* is often unread and rarely discussed. It plays a strangely peripheral part in the lives of most football people. One former professional player, Tony Cascarino, writing in *The Times* in September 2004, said that in his 19 years as a player he was 'never once handed a rulebook by a club, never took part in a training session that explained some regulations, and was never party to a meeting about the laws'.

1 **WHAT** did these players have in common between 1952 and 1961: Walley Barnes, Eric Bell, Jimmy Meadows, Bert Trautmann, Ray Wood, Roy Dwight and Len Chalmers?

The first substitute in a Football League match was Keith Peacock (Charlton Athletic) who replaced injured goalkeeper Mike Rose in the eleventh minute of a match against Bolton Wanderers. Substitutions lead to a variety of issues – warming-up procedures, where to sit, guidelines for implementing a substitution, a code of discipline for substitutes, tactical shifts that accompany a substitute's arrival, competition rules for the number of substitutes, terminology to distinguish 'players' from 'substitutes', and a whole sequence of 'What if?' questions. FIFA's *Question and Answer* booklet has more than 20 items on substitutes.

2 The English game resisted substitutions until 1965–66, when 770 substitutes were used in 2,028 Football League matches (0.33 per game). In 2002–03, **HOW MANY** substitutions were used on average per Premiership game? **(A)** 0.33, **(B)** 1.24, **(C)** 2.57, **(D)** 3.77, **(E)** 4.67 or **(F)** 5.28.

All the excitement about penalty kicks seems strange when we consider that there was no such thing during the first 28 years of organised football. Then a player deliberately handled the ball to prevent a certain goal and administrators decided it needed an appropriate punishment. The penalty kick was introduced in 1891 but opponents believed it would legitimise unsporting conduct. For many years the Corinthians goalkeeper would stand by his post to allow the attacking team to score easily from the penalty mark.

3 **WHAT** refereeing system, first mooted by the secretary-manager of Burnley in 1904, was later tested in Belgium? It was developed by Mr A. E. Fogg of Bolton and is still used. What is the system called?

Until 1996 assistant referees were known as linesmen. The change of name in that year was partly to attract more women to refereeing and partly to acknowledge the key role played by those running the line. Neutral assistants assess offsides and can spot misconduct if better placed than referees. In one match in the 1990s a Barnsley defender tackled Stoke's Simon Sturridge near the touchline and accidentally tripped up the sprinting assistant referee. Sturridge's cross resulted in a goal for Stoke City. Barnsley defenders claimed offside, but the assistant was still getting to his feet.

4 **WHAT** is the minimum number of players on a team for a match to continue?

The playwright Tom Stoppard wrote an award-winning play called *Professional Foul*. In 1990 FIFA created a new sending-off offence. Players could be dismissed if the referee answered 'Yes' to these five questions: (i) Is the attacker moving directly towards the goal? (ii) Are there fewer than two defenders between the offender and the goal? (iii) Is the ball close to, and in possession of, the attacker? (iv) Does the attacker have a reasonable shooting opportunity? And (v) Is the foul committed near enough to the goal to ensure a goal-scoring opportunity? In 1991 it was clarified that deliberate handball would be a 'professional foul' and a goalkeeper handling the ball or fouling an opponent outside the area could receive a red card.

5 **WHAT** does the refereeing acronym DOGSO stand for?

In the early 1950s, Portsmouth chairman Vernon Stokes suggested a signal to indicate an indirect free kick, namely one arm raised high in the air like a classroom swot who wants to answer a question. Referee Arthur Blythe took up the idea and in 1953 the FIFA Referees' Committee assimilated the raised-arm signal into the laws.

6 **WHICH** five English clubs have names that start and end with the same letter?

Football's passionate and emotional world generates bias and favour, but referees and referee's assistants are symbols of impartiality. They are taught to be unbiased and *seen to be* unbiased. For instance, referees shouldn't accept a lift in a team's coach or a player's car, in case they are accused of siding with one team. Ray Wood was a Huddersfield Town goalkeeper during the 1950s, and his father, Les Wood, was a League referee. The League kept them apart. Representatives of English clubs sometimes complained to the Football League secretary because they always had Welsh linesmen at games in Wales. The reply was that Welsh clubs always had English linesmen when they played in England. Touché.

7 **WHY** did Merthyr Tydfil's average attendance rise from 500 to 4,000 when the club moved from the Football League to the Southern League in 1932? Was it **(A)** the signing of a star player, **(B)** a winning team, **(C)** lower admission fees, or **(D)** more local interest?

Ole Gunnar Solskjær, veteran of well over 100 substitute appearances for Manchester United, retained a studious temperament on the bench, assessing how he could take advantage of the opposition. Goalkeepers like Nigel Martyn (Leeds United) and Kevin Poole (Bolton Wanderers) spent the 2002–03 Premier League season on the bench. In 1996 an electronic system replaced the board system at the top level, and the boards continued to be used lower down the pyramid. In local football, substitutions are gadget-free. Substitutes enter the field at the halfway line during a natural break in play. The substitution is complete when the game is restarted.

8 **WHO** won more caps for his country as a player – Matt Busby or his successor Wilf McGuinness?

A team cannot score against itself from a direct free kick (assuming no one else touches the ball after the free kick has been taken). A direct free kick should not be punished more severely than taking an indirect free kick. A team winning a *direct* free kick does so because the opposition has committed a more serious offence (e.g. handling the ball). In December 1983, during stoppage-time in the second half of a Wimbledon–Millwall game, Wimbledon took a direct free kick just outside their own penalty area. Wally Downes (Wimbledon) took the kick and chipped the ball back to goalkeeper Dave Beasant. Unfortunately it went over Beasant's head and into the net. The referee gave a goal to Millwall, making the final score 4-3 to Wimbledon rather than 4-2 … but the referee had interpreted the rule incorrectly.

9 **WHAT** was the significance of Millwall's 1-0 win against Fulham at 11.30am on 20 January 1974?

In 1969 Manchester United met Manchester City in a two-legged League Cup semi-final. The winning goal came from an indirect free kick. Not noticing the referee's raised arm, Francis Lee (City) shot for goal. Goalkeeper Alex Stepney (United) impulsively parried the ball away and Mike Summerbee (City) scored from the rebound. In an England–Holland game, in June 1990, Stuart Pearce (England) curled in an indirect free kick and the ball skidded through into the net without anybody touching it. The referee correctly awarded a goal kick.

10 In August 2018 **WHICH** world-famous sportsman made his debut for the Central Coast Mariners soccer team in New South Wales, Australia?

THE ANSWERS 143

11

MATHEMATICS AND STATISTICS

Some spectators are particularly interested in the numerical side of football. A letter-writer to the *Stoke Evening Sentinel*, in 1977, said, 'Just about the only point worth remembering about Port Vale's match with Hereford on Monday night was the fact that the attendance figure, 2,744, is a perfect cube, 14 x 14 x 14.'

1 **WHICH** three football clubs in the United Kingdom have four-letter names – one in Northern Ireland, one in northern Wales and one in northern England?

University of Amsterdam researchers discovered that goalkeepers are twice as likely to dive to their right in a penalty shoot-out when their team is behind on kicks. The penalty takers follow a more equal path when choosing the left side of the goal or the right side. In a paper for *Recreational Mathematics Magazine*, Alda Carvalho and others studied optimal shot angles, the spatial geometry of the football and ways in which goalkeepers narrow the angle. Van Basten's goal in the 1988 Euro Final was struck from an acute angle. It is also a question of swerving the ball. A 35-yard free kick for Brazil against France came from a position central to the goal area. The ball looked to be going a couple of yards wide of the right-hand post, but it swerved two yards to the left and went in via the inside of the goal post.

2 **WHICH** Brazil player scored with the swerving free kick?

Huddersfield Town won the 1924 Championship because of a better goal average. Had goal difference, rather than goal average, been in play Cardiff would have won their first League Championship because they'd scored one more goal than Huddersfield and had the same goal difference. Ivan Sharpe described the season's finale in *Forty Years in Football*: 'As the ball was crossing the line, with the goalkeeper beaten, another defender turned goalkeeper and fisted it out. Davies failed with the penalty kick, the result was a goalless draw, and the unfair fisting cost Cardiff the League Championship, because points being level, Huddersfield led on goal average reckoning by 1.818 to 1.794.'

3 **WHEN** was goal average changed to goal difference in England? Was it **(A)** 1950, **(B)** 1955, **(C)** 1960, **(D)** 1965, **(E)** 1970 or **(F)** 1975?

A Harvard University study monitored 5,000 Premier League matches involving 50 different referees between 1992 and 2006. A psychologist concluded that for every 10,000 people in the home crowd there was an increase in the average number of goals by 0.1 goals. 'In order to ensure that all games are equally fair, all referees should be equally unaffected by the spectators,' said Ryan Boyko, one of the researchers. 'Referee training could include conditioning towards certain external factors, including crowd response. Leagues should be proactive about eliminating referee bias. The potential is there for a game to be altered because of factors that subconsciously affect the referee.'

4 Davie Provan (Celtic and Scotland) once offered a quiz teaser on a football phone-in. If you write down the letters a, d, e, g, o, p and q, then here is the question: **WHICH** is the only English football club in the top four divisions where none of the letters are used?

In recent years the study of footballs has become sophisticated. Researchers have looked at the number of panels of a football, the colours, and how a football succeeds in different conditions. The original leather was replaced by synthetic materials, an increasing range of colour options became available, and pigs' bladders were changed for latex or butyl ones. FIFA-approved ball standards, introduced in 1996, covered circumference, pressure, rebounding, retention of size and shape, water absorption and weight. There is also an apocryphal story of a vegetarian player walking off the pitch when he found out he was playing with a leather ball. Another version of the tale says that he was playing in Portugal with Celta Vigo, which of course made him a Salty Vegan.

5 **WHAT** unusual feat did the brothers Kenny and Terry Hibbitt achieve when Wolves drew 1-1 with Newcastle United on 17 February 1973?

John D. Barrow's book *100 Essential Things You Didn't Know You Didn't Know About Sport* looks at sport statistics. John Nash, a Nobel prize-winner, calculated the equilibrium for the contest between the penalty-taker and goalkeeper, and Nash reckoned that the penalty taker should put 37 per cent of shots to the left, 29 per cent down the middle and 34 per cent to the right. The goalkeeper's best strategy was to dive left 44 per cent of the time, stay in the middle for 13 per cent and dive right for 43 per cent.

6 Ipswich Town goalkeeper Paul Cooper was in good form in the 1979–80 season. **HOW MANY** penalties did he save out of ten?

One particularly close finish was the last match of the 1988–89 season when Arsenal won the Premier League Championship at Liverpool. The match took place in the wake of the Hillsborough Disaster and the two teams' goal difference was so tight that inside stoppage time Liverpool, 1-0 down, seemed certain to win the Championship. Then Arsenal scored a second goal and suddenly the title was Arsenal's.

7 **WHEN** Liverpool beat West Ham United in the 2006 FA Cup Final, nine Liverpool players had double letters in their surnames. Who were they? (9)

In 1964–65, in the days of two points for a win, Hearts (50 points) and Kilmarnock (48 points) played for the Scottish League championship, and 37,275 people attended the final match. Hearts had a better goal average (1.9149) than Kilmarnock (1.8182), and Hearts started well when Jensen hit the post. But Killie scored twice in two minutes midway through the first half. Hearts now had the same number of points as Killie but a worse goal average (1.84 to Kilmarnock's 1.88). In stoppage time in the second half Kilmarnock goalkeeper Bobby Ferguson saved brilliantly to ensure that Kilmarnock became champions. Killie manager Willie Waddell charged across the pitch to celebrate with his goalie.

8 **CAN** you name a Scottish League club containing no letters from the word 'football'?

In a *British Medical Journal* paper (December 2004) Dr Francisco Belda Maruenda argued that a referee cannot assess the relative position of two defenders, two attackers and the ball *at the same time*. Maruenda, a specialist in family medicine, applied the response times of five types of eye movement to the speed of the players' movements. Is Maruenda's argument worth further investigation? Assistants improve with experience. If one offside in 20 is debatable, is that a reason for introducing video evidence for every one (as suggested)?

9 **WHICH** four calls can be reviewed by the Video Assistant Referee (VAR)? (4)

When Derby County won the 1971–72 League Championship their top five League and Cup goal scorers were Alan Durban, Kevin Hector, Alan Hinton, John O'Hare and Frank Wignall (but not in that order). O'Hare scored an allegedly unlucky number of goals, and Wignall scored exactly half of Durban's haul. Hinton scored nine in open play and almost as many from penalty kicks. Hinton's League goals were statistically three-fifths of Hector's League and Cup goals in total. These top five goal scorers scored 60 between them.

10 **HOW** many League and Cup goals did Durban, Hector, Hinton, O'Hare and Wignall score individually? (5)

THE ANSWERS ☞ 144

12

WARTIME FOOTBALL

In September 1939, at the start of the Second World War, all football was stopped for five days. When play resumed crowds were limited. National Service was considered more important than football, and travel was limited to 50 miles (80.5km). A few representative games continued, and top-class footballers gathered around Aldershot because professional players had been called up to that area. Germany's air-raid bombing of Britain started in July 1940.

1 **WHAT** was the date of the 1942 Scottish Summer Cup Final: **(A)** 30 April, **(B)** 22 May, **(C)** 13 June or **(D)** 4 July?

The Falklands Conflict began on 2 April 1982 and one suggestion for deciding possession of the islands was a football match between Britain and Argentina. The British Antarctic Survey (BAS) team played matches in South Georgia from 1970. Competition reached its peak around 1976, when BAS played 20 games on the Whaling Station pitch near the Grytviken base. Opponents included Poland, USA, East Germany and South Africa. The BAS team was selected from about 20 men on base. They changed into black and white shirts in an old cinema and drove to the pitch in a tractor and trailer. On 3 April 1982, South Georgia was captured by Argentinian forces and retaken by the British three weeks later. In the island game's history the best-named team was surely Two Boats United.

2 In 2009 Jimmy Curtis was appointed to manage **WHICH** team?

On Christmas Day 1941, Bristol City players set out on a 106-mile (171km) journey to Southampton to play football. Two cars failed to arrive in time for the match, so Bristol City's team consisted of two City players, five Southampton amateurs, the Southampton trainer, and three spectators, including a soldier and a schoolmaster. The missing players arrived 80 minutes late. Southampton won 5-2. That Christmas Day saw Bradford Park Avenue and Huddersfield Town play two matches on the same day. The morning match had an attendance of 2,080 and the afternoon game brought in 5,300 spectators.

3 Rangers drew 2-2 with Hibernian in the final of the Scottish Summer Cup in 1941–42. There had to be a definite winner. **WHAT** two methods were used? (2)

Eddie Mason joined the Dragoon Guards in 1912 and then served his country for four years during the First World War. He fought in two Battles of the Marne, the Battle of Ypres and the Battle of Aisne. He survived it all with barely a stitch. In 1919, however, he joined Hull City, had a bad injury in his first game and missed the rest of the season. During the First World War football was played by women who worked in factories, especially the touring Dick, Kerr's Ladies teams. On Boxing Day 1920 a crowd of 54,000 watched a women's game.

4 **WHERE** were Dick, Kerr's Ladies based?

Vic Barney was due to join Arsenal when the Second World War broke out. After the fighting had stopped he took charge of a football stadium in Naples (Italy). On his return to England he played for Reading, Bristol City and Grimsby Town, where he was given cases of fish. When living in Oxfordshire he had two years as Headington United captain and enjoyed it very much. He lived about 6 miles (9.7km) north-west of Witney. When playing away he often missed the last train home, but a porter set up a coal fire and provided coats for Barney to sleep on in the waiting room. In the morning he'd go to the local railway canteen.

5 **WHICH** footballer won promotion from the Fourth Division with two different clubs in the 1960s, and, as a professional cricketer, had the same name as a first-class championship ground?

In 1940–41 the FA allowed some recreation through Sunday football, more than two decades before Sunday football was legitimised. In October 1940 the FA decided that all matches would have to stop during air raid alerts. In December spotters were used to pinpoint enemy aircraft so that matches could continue or crowds could disperse from grounds safely. On Christmas Day 1940, Norwich City beat Brighton 18-0 with a double hat-trick from Chadwick and hat-tricks from Marshall, Roberts and Plunkett.

6 Which European country has a record of two wins and two draws from its four matches against Brazil?

In the 1942–43 season Blackpool met Sheffield Wednesday in a two-legged Football League North Cup Final. Stanley Matthews laid on two goals for Blackpool, but Blackpool only drew, and Matthews would miss the second leg while playing for England. 'Many people thought Blackpool had thrown away their chance,' said a reporter, but Blackpool won the second leg 2-1. However, Stoke City publicly announced their dissatisfaction with Stanley Matthews. He had not played for the club during wartime and had guested for other teams. There was talk of a £15,000 transfer to Blackpool at the end of the war.

7 **HOW** many times was Ryan Giggs a substitute? **(A)** 3, **(B)** 42, **(C)** 81 or **(D)** 110?

John Kirkham was signed by Wolves in March 1936 when he was 17. He joined Bournemouth FC in October 1938 and then had an astonishing wartime career as a soldier. He was first reported missing in 1942 in North Africa, captured by the Germans, and he spent 18 months in an Italian prisoner-of-war camp. He escaped three times, and on the third avoided capture and joined French and Italian guerrillas in the mountains. Known as the 'Houdini of the prisoner-of-war camps', he met up with Allied Forces in Italy. In his only post-war football season he escaped one or two centre-halves too; he scored 31 goals in 60 games.

8 **WHICH** famous match featured this line-up? Hatch, Colby, Cleeve, Brady, Van Beck, Hayes, Rey, Wolchek, Fileu, Harmon, Hernandez.

'This game should never have started,' wrote Roy Peskett in 1945. 'Frequently the pitch was completely blotted out by waves of fog. Many of the Arsenal players told me that often they could see only five of their opponents. Players loomed up out of the smokescreen, flitted into view, then vanished into the Tottenham gloom.' That match was a 4-3 win for Moscow Dynamo. The Russians continued their tour with a 10-1 win at Cardiff City, a 3-3 draw at Chelsea and a 2-2 draw at Glasgow Rangers. The crowd at Chelsea was around 85,000. 'When we were two goals down we compared the game to Stalingrad, when the Germans were outside our gates,' said the Moscow Dynamo trainer Michail Yakushkin. 'We were not downhearted and certain our time would come.'

9 At the old Wembley Stadium **HOW** many steps were there to the Royal Box?

• •

Moving on from the Second World War there was hope for improved international relations with the resurrection of the World Cup, in 1950, 12 years after the last tournament. In the 1950 World Cup Final Uruguay beat Brazil 1-0 (in Brazil) thanks to a goal by Alcides Ghiggia (also known as Zhiggia). 'Only three men have ever silenced the Maracanã,' Ghiggia once said, 'the Pope, Frank Sinatra and me.' Ghiggia said that Brazil still welcomed him decades later. When he showed his passport a young woman on the desk kept looking at him. 'Are you *the* Ghiggia?' the woman asked. 'Yes, but it was a long time ago,' said Ghiggia. 'No, no,' the woman said, holding her hand to her heart, 'It still hurts us.' In 1958, when Ghiggia was playing for Italy, he was sent off against Northern Ireland.

10 The whole match was televised by the BBC except for the first ten minutes. **WHY** were those minutes missing?

THE ANSWERS ☞ 145

13

STRANGE INCIDENTS

An old cartoon shows a man in a hospital bed with a dart in his head. 'Tell me, doctor,' says a concerned woman at the bedside, 'Will he ever referee again?' Sometimes the joke isn't funny. Items tossed on to pitches include leeks, British Rail cutlery, ball-bearings, cigarette lighters, hot dogs, mobile phones, meat pies and toilet rolls. A dustbin lid was once thrown on to the Ilkeston Town pitch. Spurs goalkeeper Pat Jennings was once knocked out by a bottle. Under the Football (Offences) Act 1991, throwing an object towards the playing area (or towards other spectators) is an offence unless there is a lawful excuse (with the onus on the accused to prove it).

1 During a 1962–63 League Cup semi-final, a Northern Ireland striker, playing for Aston Villa, threw snowballs at Sunderland fans who had given him some banter. The referee laughed it off. **WHAT** was the striker's name?

The Baseball Ground was the home of Derby County from 1895 to 1997. The pitch was sometimes more swamp soccer than football fever. In 1977 groundsman

Bob Smith was called on to the pitch during a match with Manchester City. Smith was asked to find and mark the penalty spot after Gary Owen had fouled Archie Gemmell for a penalty. 'Well, this is extraordinary,' said commentator John Motson. 'There is certainly some football history being made here and I'm sure the penalty spot has never been painted during a First Division match before. Well, who's been unsettled by that – Daley or Corrigan?' When Daley scored the penalty, Motson added, 'Number four from the number four.'

2 **HOW** did John Motson become a football commentator?

At times two political foes have played each other at football. Japan beat North Korea 3-0 in Qatar in 1993, and the teams met again in 2005 in a World Cup qualifier. North Korea saw Japan as an imperialist aggressor and Japan saw North Korea as a Stalinesque dictatorship. Other politically hot fixtures have included Iran's 2-1 victory against the United States in June 1998 and a 0-0 draw between South Korea and North Korea, when the two sets of players held their rivals' hands when they walked on to the field.

3 During the 1986 World Cup finals **WHAT** unusual chant was created by England fans to celebrate two England players?

On 26 April 2003 a match between Tranmere Rovers and Mansfield Town was abandoned at half time because a spectator had climbed one of the floodlight pylons. He jumped the gap from the floodlight pylon to the roof of the Cow Shed Stand, and then he didn't know what to do. Seven thousand spectators were asked to leave at half time and the referee abandoned the match. In court the climber pleaded guilty to a charge of drunk and disorderly behaviour.

4 **HOW** much was his fine – **(A)** £200, **(B)** £400, **(C)** £600 or **(D)** £800?

Certain ill-conceived competition rules have provoked players into planning own goals. One example was the 1998 Tiger Cup. Thailand and Indonesia both wished to finish second to avoid favourites Vietnam in the next round. With a few minutes left, the score at 2-2, Indonesia attacked their own goal. Despite fervent defence by Thailand, Indonesia's goalkeeper got hold of the ball and threw it into his own net. The authorities punished the teams involved.

5 When Leicester City drew 2-2 with Aston Villa in March 1976 **WHAT** strange feat did Chris Nicholl of Aston Villa achieve?

• •

When Mark Walters arrived at Ibrox Park to play for Rangers he thought he would fit in easily, but the young black winger faced a barrage of abuse. 'Within days of his arrival he was nicknamed Jaffa,' wrote Stuart Cosgrove, author of *Hampden Babylon*, 'black on the outside and orange on the inside.' Thirty years earlier Celtic had signed Giles Heron, a black American striker from the US amateur team Chicago Maroons. Heron's son, Gil Scott-Heron, was a radical singer. Paul Elliot (Aston Villa and Pisa) signed for Celtic and said later that the racial abuse he suffered in Scotland was far worse than he had faced in England and Italy.

6 Rangers and Celtic are known as the Old Firm. Since the early 1980s **WHICH** two clubs are considered to be the New Firm?

René van der Kerkhof played for Holland in the 1978 FIFA World Cup Final. He broke a bone in his hand against Iran in the first match and played with a special plaster from Holland. 'I played five matches with this plaster and then there was an incident during the final,' said van der Kerkhof. 'The referee said that I couldn't play with my hand in plaster because Argentina's captain, Passarella, had pointed it out to him. The referee agreed with Passarella because he was pro-Argentina anyway. Ruud Krol, our captain, made him understand that if I wasn't allowed to play, none of the Dutch team would play. Of course, they were very shocked, and they argued for about ten to 12 minutes. Finally they decided that I had to have some tape to strengthen my plaster. I didn't understand why this was necessary because this tape made my hand very tight and it frustrated me.'

7 **HOW** many times have Holland finished runners-up in a World Cup Final?

Bradford Park Avenue FC was wound up on 3 May 1974, but an archaeological excavation of the pitch took place nearly 40 years later. Neville Gabie, author of *Posts*, suggested working with an archaeologist and a sports historian. A nappy pin was found in one goal area and everybody was mystified. Then Susan Farr, daughter of Bradford PA goalie Chick Farr, explained. Apparently the elastic in her father's shorts had caused them to fall down, so the trainer took a nappy pin on to the field. For weeks afterwards the goalkeeper was showered with nappy pins, either through the post or on to the pitch, and Chick Farr kept them in an old tobacco tin. The archaeological survey also discovered stones, bricks, gutter fragments, tin cans, bottle tops, light bulbs, glass fragments, pen tops, marbles (once thrown at goalies), plastic knives and forks, early decimal coins, and four football-boot studs.

8 In 1970 **WHICH** club entered the Football League when Bradford Park Avenue left it?

A bizarre five-minute delay occurred during the 2005 High Wycombe Sunday Challenge Cup Final when a fight broke out in the Causeway Stadium main stand. The rumpus disturbed the players, a few of whom came to the touchline to yell instructions to the unruly participants. Roles were reversed. Spectators were now the players, and footballers the onlookers, offering advice such as 'Sort it out'. The referee restarted play with an indirect free kick for offside.

9 Lee Bowyer, Derek Hales and Graeme Le Saux all fought with team-mates on the pitch. **CAN** you name their sparring partners? (3)

Manchester United physiotherapist Jim McGregor was a star of the 1991 Rumbelows League Cup Final against Sheffield Wednesday. Goalkeeper Les Sealey flew into a rage when told he should leave the field for attention to a leg wound, but McGregor calmed the goalkeeper down and bandaged the leg on the field. Had the player hit his physio, as seemed likely at one point, the referee would have sent the player off.

10 The highest attendance at Old Trafford is 76,962 in 1939. **WHICH** two teams were playing?

THE ANSWERS ☞ 146

14

WHO ARE THEY? (PART 1)

This player came from Sheffield, joined a local team and became a full England international. The fans called him Zico in honour of his long hair, international status and long throw-ins. He won seven England under-21 caps, League titles in England and Scotland, and made four England B appearances. But an ankle injury set him back. He and his wife had a big house with an indoor swimming pool and a snooker room. He had four operations at the end of his playing days, and he retired when he was told, 'Carry on and you'll end up in a wheelchair.' His autobiography, *Boozing, Betting and Brawling*, was revealing.

1 **WHO** is he?

This player made over 800 League appearances and played in 40 internationals. Born in Coventry, he played as a full-back or defensive midfielder. He was second in the list of outfield appearances with over 1,000 to his name. His goal tally was over 100, boosted by free kicks and penalties. In his last match he came on as a late sub and made the home crowd happy by curving a low free kick inside the right goalpost. He got a yellow card for celebrating too much and then gave the referee a hug. He certainly didn't have a hand of God, but he managed in the land of cod, followed by an Iron hand and Media City UK.

2 **WHO** is he?

He was born in Swindon, Wiltshire, and his father rode for a local speedway team. His Christian names were Roger and Patrick, but everybody knew him as Ernie. At Coventry three-wheeled cars were parked around the pitch for disabled people, so he toe-poked the ball under the cars, opened the door and asked if they could take his throw-ins for him because he was knackered. He ran a Ledbury pub for nine years and said it was 'like giving a match to an arsonist'. In October 1970, he and his team-mate Willie devised an unusual free kick. They practised it in training and it worked a treat. He died in 2018.

3 **WHO** was he?

This man grew up in Eastwood, Nottinghamshire. He signed for Notts County and then joined a West Midlands club. In 1967–68 he scored in every FA Cup round. In extra time in the final his right-footed shot rebounded from a defender and he whacked the ball home with his left. He headed the ball a lot and shot with either foot. Later he worked as a window-cleaner and chose the slogan 'he never missed the corners'. But the frequent heading of heavy balls caught up with him. By the age of 59 he didn't know he'd ever been a footballer. Heading a ball over 1,000 times a year could cause concussions and early-onset dementia. Other players, such as Ernie Moss and Kevin Moore, had been affected. In 2017 a BBC documentary fronted by Alan Shearer helped to raise awareness of footballers and dementia.

4 **WHO** was he?

This man was a famous Scotland international during the period from 1896–1908. His clubs included Queen's Park, Newcastle United and Rangers. When he first arrived at Queen's Park, wearing his school cap, the doorman couldn't believe he was a player, but the player developed speed, courage, swerve and shooting power. He scored a hat-trick for Scotland against England in April 1900, a performance unsurpassed until the 1928 Wembley Wizards. 'Nothing short of a mound of Limburg cheese, which they say is so strong to smell, would keep the Scots out of the English goal,' wrote *Athletic News* in 1900. He started a newsagent's business and his name is still seen on shopfronts.

5 **WHO** was he?

He was 6ft 4in (1.93m) with gravitas and he reached Class 1 refereeing status by the age of 24. He was calm and polite inside the cauldron and claimed industrial deafness. He was the Jeeves of Scottish football. One day, when Johnny Hamilton (Hearts) had left his false teeth in the dressing room, the referee said, 'Mister Hamilton, your time has come to be reunited with your teeth.' Another time, when the referee asked for a Celtic player's name, he got the reply, 'Roy Rogers'. 'Well, Mr Rogers,' the official said, 'it's time for you to saddle up and join Trigger in the stables.' Another time he turned down a penalty appeal by saying, 'Not today, Swan Lake.'

6 **WHO** was he?

A club was formed in 1871 and international matches were played from 1892. In September 1925 England played Wales in an international at Southampton. The match had an unusual feel. The 500 spectators handclapped at times but otherwise it was very quiet. There are now special FA tournaments and these games are a real asset. The equivalent of a professional foul is to stop momentarily as if seeing a flag and then continue playing. The 2017–18 Challenge Cup Final saw Bristol City DFC play St John's DFC.

7 **WHAT** kind of footballers were competing?

He played with three youth teams in the East Midlands and then in the professional game as a central defender and, later, as a central striker. He joined United in a university city and, at the end of the 1989–90 season, was the first ever player to score in a Wembley play-off final. In his 20-year career he played over 600 games for seven clubs and scored nearly 200 goals. He broke his leg in September 1992 and his neck in December 1999. He carried on until his 'bones started to talk to him'. He also presents a daytime television programme.

8 **WHO** is he?

Uncle and nephew shared the same surname. At Wembley, to the chants of 'Come on Wednesday,' the nephew almost saved the Wednesday player's shot, touching it on to the post and into the net. He played for ten clubs but, sadly, died of a heart attack when only 43. His uncle scored twice in a European Cup Final at Wembley in the mid-1960s. But the uncle was also unlucky with health as he broke a leg in a freak accident and later died from a heart attack at the age of 53. The nephew's last four appearances for a northern team were a Cup winners' Cup Final, two League Cup finals and an FA Cup quarter-final.

9 **WHO** were they – uncle and nephew?

What can you say about one of the best players in the world in recent years? He is only 5ft 7in (1.7m) tall but has scored a winning goal at the highest level with only a few minutes of extra time remaining. He came through a Spanish youth academy and played 674 appearances for his club, eventually moving to Japan. He won over 30 trophies and was much revered by colleagues, staff and spectators. He was also the UEFA player of the 2012 Euro tournament. Playing against Scotland, in October 2010, he passed the ball into the net to make the score 2-0 and Scotland's visitors won 3-2.

10 **WHO** is he?

THE ANSWERS ☞ 147

15

MISCELLANEOUS 1

An example of a team levelling the scores came with a match between Woking and Grays Athletic in August 2007. There was no score after 85 minutes and then Woking's Paul Lorraine was injured. The referee resumed the game with an uncontested dropped ball, but Matt Pattison's attempt to return the ball to Grays goalkeeper Ross Flitney went awry. The ball soared over a surprised Flitney and into the net. There was a heated response from the Grays players, so the Woking manager agreed to concede a goal. Woking goalkeeper Nick Gindre covered his eyes while Grays equalised at 1-1.

1 **WHO** are the only two men to score a hat-trick of headers in the Premier League? The first man was for Everton in 1997, the second one for West Brom in 2016. (2)

In August 2007 Clive Clarke, on a three-month loan from Sunderland to Leicester City, was playing against Nottingham Forest. He collapsed during the Carling Cup tie after he'd collided with his own goalkeeper. He had a cardiac arrest and was treated with a defibrillator in the Leicester dressing room. The match was abandoned at half time, and Clarke's playing career was effectively over at 27. He'd won one cap for the Republic of Ireland. When the match was replayed Leicester City allowed the Forest team to resurrect the 1-0 scoreline of the original match. The Football League and Nottingham Forest had agreed. Leicester City won 3-2.

2 **WHAT** soccer-related job did Clive Clarke take up after his retirement from football?

Imagine you are standing in a line with your team-mates, waiting for the national anthem of your country to be played. You are ready to perform at the highest level and it means a lot to you, your family, your nation and your colleagues. The hairs on your neck are standing up, you've been given a game plan, you've remembered your lucky charm, you're weighing up your opponents, and then the music begins.

3 'Himno Istmeño' ('Hymn of the Isthmus') was written in 1925 by Santos Jorge. England came away with a substantial victory where this was played in recent times. **WHAT** was the score?

Pitch invasions were more common in the 1960s and 1970s, and one pivotal match was the Newcastle United and Nottingham Forest FA Cup tie in March 1974. Hundreds of spectators ran on to the pitch, the players returned to the dressing rooms, and the police took eight minutes to clear the pitch. Twenty-three people went to hospital, another 103 were treated on the pitch, and the police made 39 arrests. The 54,000-strong crowd created an intimidating atmosphere, and ten-man Newcastle came from 3-1 down to win 4-3. The result was declared null and void, but Newcastle were given the chance to 'replay' on a neutral ground. That match ended

0-0 and a third match was won by Newcastle United. Nottingham Forest played three matches in that sixth-round tie and none of them was on their home ground.

4 **WHICH** Newcastle United 'number five' was sent off in the 55th minute? He shares his surname with the Dukes of Norfolk.

Many goalkeepers think they could be excellent strikers if they got the chance. Some injured keepers went on the wing and notched the only goal of their career. Sometimes the regular keeper charged up the other end to see if they could help the team. For instance, Mart Poom headed a last-minute equaliser for Sunderland against his former club Derby County, and Carlisle United goalkeeper Jimmy Glass, sent up by his manager, latched on to a rebound to score the goal that kept Carlisle in the Football League in May 1999.

5 The world's top three goal-scoring goalkeepers come from Central or South America. They include Jorge Campos (Mexico), Rogério Ceni (Brazil) and José Luis Chilavert (Paraguay). **HOW** many did these three keepers score on aggregate? Was it **(A)** 244, **(B)** 122, **(C)** 61 or **(D)** 30?

Administrators and referees must be seen to be unbiased. But conspiracy theories abound. One states that Rangers and Celtic were kept apart in Scottish Cup draws between 1947 and 1989 because that was the desired Scottish Cup Final. Another suggested that the FA had never wanted a third-tier team in an FA Cup Final, pointing to refereeing decisions in FA Cup semi-finals involving third-tier teams: two dubious free kicks enabled Sunderland to beat Third Division (South)

Millwall (1937); a debatable West Brom penalty kick and a Port Vale 'goal' disallowed for offside (1954); a late shot by Bottom (York City) which seemed over the line for a winner against Newcastle United (1955); and a shot by Howard (Chesterfield) which hit the crossbar and then bounced over the Middlesbrough line (1997).

6 **WHICH** two third-tier clubs won the League Cup in 1967 and 1969? (2)

Publishers try to find the right book title. It could be Ian Ure's *Ure's Truly*, Frank Worthington's *One Hump or Two*, or Dave Wagstaffe's *Waggy's Tales*. The more serious include Harry Redknapp's *Always Managing*, and Frank Lampard's *Totally Frank*. Particularly meaningful are the tales of Tony Adams in *Addicted*, Paul Merson's *How Not to be a Professional Footballer* and a number of books spawned by Paul Gascoigne. In *Clown Prince of Soccer*, written in 1955, Len Shackleton wrote a chapter called 'What Directors Know about Football' and then he left the page blank. In 2018 came *Feed the Beast* by Jon Parkin, who was in his 19th spell at various clubs.

7 It's 5 miles (8km) from the Amex Stadium to the Dripping Pan. **WHICH** two clubs play at these grounds (2)?

Tony Brown's book *Red – Missed* contains the story of players sent off between 1979–80 and 2000–01. Seven players succumbed to ten red cards during that period and three others had more than ten sending-offs. Two feisty players chalked up 13 red cards in long careers. One, a long-serving Leicester City player, was once given an 11-match ban for breaking an opponent's jaw and the other signed for Walsall, Colchester United, Exeter City, Southend United and various other teams.

8 **WHICH** man was sent off 11 times in a career that included one red card for Sheffield United and ten when playing for Wimbledon?

Prime Ministers of the distant past were more likely to follow cricket, golf, tennis, yachting or rowing than football. However, Harold Wilson, as a small child, was aware that Huddersfield Town had won three successive Championships in the 1920s. Later, in 1966, when England won the World Cup, Wilson wryly commented that England had only won the trophy under a Labour government. Ted Heath was a yachtsman and Jim Callaghan was more likely to follow rugby union or tennis. Margaret Thatcher disliked all sports at a time when football needed help, John Major was a Chelsea fan who watched matches at Stamford Bridge, Tony Blair followed Newcastle United, and Gordon Brown was a loyal club fan.

9 **WHICH** club did Gordon Brown support?

Mr and Mrs William Keetley had 11 sons and one daughter. Five of the sons played professional football during the 1920s and 1930s. Joe played for six clubs, Tom two, Harold one, Frank four, and Charlie three. Altogether the five sons played for 14 different clubs. Between them they played 904 matches and scored 514 goals. Frank Keetley scored six for Lincoln City when beating Halifax 9-1. After the match a local poet said, 'I have told of how Frank Keetley, shoots so well and passes neatly.'

10 The Keetley footballers were born in an East Midlands town which was made a city in 1977. **WHICH** city is it?

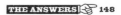

THE ANSWERS ☞ 148

16

WOMEN AND FOOTBALL

On 11 February 1950 Shirley Wootten travelled by coach to Willington, County Durham, with Wimbledon supporters on board (more women than men). They intended to watch a match in the last 16 of the FA Amateur Cup. They set off at midnight because they couldn't afford an overnight stay. They were decked out in blue and white scarves, blue and white hats, blue and white rattles, blue and white balloons and blue and white rosettes. It took about 12 hours to travel from South London to the North West. Wimbledon lost 4-2 and failed to reach the last eight. But 13 years later, in 1963, Wimbledon won the FA Amateur Cup for the first time, beating Sutton United 4-2.

1 Eddie Reynolds scored all four goals for Wimbledon against Sutton in 1963. **WHAT** was particularly unusual about the goals?

The Women's Cup started in November 1970 and the first final saw Southampton win 4-1 against Ayrshire's Stewarton Thistle. One of the new wave of women's footballers was Paddy McGroarty, who was born in England but lived for many years in Scotland.

McGroarty, a cousin of the Scottish men's international Pat Crerand, was a nun, but she left to join the army when she discovered that she couldn't play football in a nunnery. On 23 June 1973 she played for England and scored twice in an 8-0 win against Scotland.

2 The 8-0 women's fixture was played at Manor Park ground in the Midlands. It was fitting for a nun that the town was known as Sunny Nunny. **WHAT** was the name of the football club?

Members of staff at one professional club were intrigued by a letter addressed to Bill Bennett. It was baffling because the club had no player called Bill Bennett. The letter hung around in the players' pigeon holes for about three months and then someone decided to open it. The letter was from a woman who thanked Bill Bennett for the fantastic time she'd had at the Butlin's camp, and it was the first time she'd been so close to a professional footballer. That sort of thing probably happened a lot.

3 Over 40 Bennetts have played professional football, including Woody Bennett, Martellus Bennett and Jug Bennett – but no Bill Bennett. **WHAT** was the name of the Bennett who scored one goal and made another when Coventry City won the 1987 FA Cup Final?

By the mid-1970s the Women's Football Association was losing its top players. Edna Nellis, Rose Reilly and Sue Lopez went to play in Italy. The cost of staging an international with Sweden meant that the WFA was down to its last £40. Continuing on the Bennett theme, a 12-year-old girl called Theresa Bennett was stopped from playing with the boys. The Bennett case revolved around section 44 of the UK Sex Discrimination

Act, but other countries didn't have such restrictions. Denmark and France mixed boys and girls until under-14s and Germany until under-17s. But the FA won their case, and it wasn't until 1991 that the FA allowed mixed football for under-11s.

4 **WHICH** nationality were Nellis and Reilly?

Phil Thompson, a Liverpool and England player, watched Leeside FC and in particular he watched Margaret Ireland playing for Leeside. The story was that Thompson had been the referee for a charity match and had cautioned Ireland in order to get her name and telephone number. They became engaged and were married on 26 June 1981. That was the year that Thompson and the Liverpool players won the European Cup … again.

5 **WHO** scored the winning goal of the 1981 European Cup Final?

Mabel Smith was 93 when she died in 2013. She was known to many Stoke City supporters because she sold half-time draw tickets and had lots of badges on her scarf. She was also a coach courier for away trips. She started following the Potters in 1949 and missed very few matches, home or away. She was on the supporters' club committee for about 25 years and was named *The Sentinel* Stoke City fan of 2008. The former Stoke City manager, Tony Pulis, spoke highly of her. 'Mabel was a wonderful person who was always very supportive and would make great little comments whenever I bumped into her,' said Pulis. 'She used to take a flask which was supposed to have milk in it, but actually had Baileys. Her blood wasn't red, it was red and white.'

6 **CAN** you name five out of seven English clubs which have traditionally worn red and white stripes? (5)

In the late 1990s Vanessa Hardwick won a landmark coaching case and damages against the Football Association. The Equal Opportunities Commission helped her prove that she was discriminated against when she took her FA coaching certificate. Her marks were higher than some men's marks, but only three out of 2,000 advanced coaching licences were held by women. 'The course was physically and emotionally demanding,' Vanessa Hardwick told the *Independent*, 'and not being one of the boys – not being in with the innuendos – made it more stressful. I suffered because I was assessed on my ability to play men's football in their style and not women's, which is vastly different.'

7 **WHICH** female referee was an assistant referee for the 2012 FA Trophy Final and assistant referee for the 2018 Women's Champions League Final?

In 2007 this footballer played against an excellent Japan team in China. Her team was 1-0 down when she equalised with her left foot ten minutes from time. Then she took off her left boot and kissed it. Her second goal came three minutes later when she shot with her left foot. Her attempt rebounded towards her right foot, so she scored with that foot. Then she took off her right boot and kissed it. The match ended 2-2. This Watford-born player won 117 England caps and scored 46 international goals. She played for Wembley Ladies and Arsenal Ladies and scored 76 goals in 51 matches in the USA college system. Her injuries included right knee, a broken leg and stress fractures. Described as the

Maradona – or Messi – of the women's game, she was awarded an MBE in the 2008 birthday honours.

8 **WHO** is she?

This player is known as 'Pelé's cousin' or 'Pelé in skirts' and has dual Brazil and Sweden citizenships. Between 2004 and 2008 she scored 210 goals in 103 matches for Umeå IK. She won silver medals at the 2004 and 2008 Summer Olympics and was FIFA's world player of the year for five years in the 2000s. She was one of eight people to carry the Olympic Games flag in the Rio Olympics. In over a hundred internationals she's achieved almost a goal a game. She usually wears the number ten shirt. In 2018 she won the 'best female player' award for the sixth time.

9 **WHO** is she?

Women's football has been played since the early 17th century but men have tried to quash the women's game. Church documents for South Lanarkshire, Scotland, showed that women played soccer on 21 August 1628. A British Ladies football club was formed in 1895 but it wasn't until the First World War, while men were away soldiering, that women thrived on playing the men's game. Recent women players include the American Julie Foudy, a Fair Play award winner in 1997, who won 271 international caps for the USA women's team, fought child labour abuses and promoted causes for disabled children and female athletes.

10 **WHICH** American woman won 354 caps and scored 130 goals?

THE ANSWERS ☞ 149

17

QUOTATIONS

This man was very popular with Everton fans because he scored a winner against Liverpool in front of 54,000 at Goodison Park. Unfortunately, after scoring, he went to the Liverpool fans rather than the Evertonians, and he got hit in the face by a meat pie. At Manchester City he was nicknamed Imre Banana during the era of inflatables. He played for 16 clubs. But when he was the manager of Matlock Town he spoke about a new experience: 'Never before in my 18 years in football have I been on a team leading 3-0 with six minutes left, playing against ten men, that hasn't won.'

1 **WHO** is he?

Some managers spoke like Mrs Malaprop in Sheridan's *The Rivals*. One boss defended an error by saying, 'Nobody's inflammable.' Another gave a Friday team talk: 'You know how you usually veer to the left or veer to the right, tomorrow I want you to veer straight forward.' Another gaffer needed a new winger because there was 'A dearth of a shortage in this club'. One manager said, 'Allegations are all very well, but I'd like to know who the alligators are.' And the reason for a 6-1 win was 'The harmonium in the dressing room.' A director pointed out that 'We've been drawn against Standard Liege, first leg in Standard.' Another director saw his club was drawn against Torpedo Moscow but couldn't find Torpedo on the map.

2 **WHICH** team has been managed by Eric Worthington, Tom Tranter, Martin Reagan, John Bilton, Ted Copeland, Hope Powell and Mark Sampson?

It is always difficult to get the attention of players when the manager has words to say. 'Listen up, listen up,' shouts the manager, 'No laughing at the referee this week, no answering back … hey, turn that mobile off, I'm giving a team talk here.' Then another player says, 'Keep your phone on, it might be his mum.' The manager sighs loudly and starts to talk about tactics but he is interrupted by a player. 'I've got a question, Gaffer,' says the player. 'Is it safe to leave stuff in the dressing room?'

3 At the start of 2018–19 season **WHICH** six Football League teams had names ending with an 'e'? (6)

Bill Shankly always had something interesting to say. Here's one passage from the former Liverpool manager: 'My aim in life was, even in the Army, when you went in the Services during the war, you've got some horrible jobs. You'd go in the cookhouse to dry about 6,000 dishes, you see, and the latrines, to clean them out well. If I had a job to do, even it was scrubbing the floor, I wanted my floor to be cleaner than yours. If everybody thinks along those lines and does all the small jobs to the best of their ability, that's honesty, then the whole world would be better, and football would be better.

What we want is hard work, and no football club is ever successful without hard work.'

4 Shankly, born in Glenbuck, Ayrshire, played for Cronberry Eglinton. His second professional club was Preston North End. **WHAT** was his first?

Sir Harold Thompson was a blunt Yorkshireman who spent 50 years dedicated to football. Chairman of the Football Association, he believed in true amateurism and, in 1948, started a successful amateur club called Pegasus. In 1978 Professor Thompson gave a speech: 'In some of the uninformed public Press, I have lately been described as a geriatric lofty intellectual. I am sure that stigma is not appropriate, but if it is, I will today come down from the ivory tower that I have never known, and I can only hope that you will not now go to the other extreme and describe me in the terms of that wonderful book of Cornford's, *Microcosmographia Academica*, written in 1908 about Cambridge politics, as a "young man in a hurry" or even as "an Adullamite".'

5 In 2018 Neville Gabie and Alan Ward unveiled a granite sculpture bearing the words 'written in stone, interpreted worldwide, brought back to Cambridge'. **WHICH** body of legislation was first documented in Cambridge in 1848?

In the 1950s the financing of professional football was largely via gate receipts, transfer fees and money from local businessmen. From the early 1960s football clubs included wealthy millionaires, such as John Moores of Everton. In February 1924 Moores asked small boys to hand out pools coupons outside Manchester United's football ground. By March 1927 about 20,000 coupons a week were returned, and by the 1950s the figure was about ten million a week. 'I never interfere with managers,' Moores said, after Harry Catterick was appointed manager. 'Directors should not do so, they are really just amateurs in the football world.' Everton were Football League champions (1962–63 and 1969–70) and FA Cup winners (1966).

6 **WHICH** Everton and England player was banned for life and imprisoned for fixing matches while with a previous club?

Archie Goodall was born in Belfast and his brother John in London. They were raised in Scotland but forced to represent their birthplace countries. Archie won ten caps for Ireland and John 14 for England. In 1898 John Goodall reflected on his early days in football: 'One's first football match is remembered, doubtless, with some horror. I have a hazy recollection of putting on a pair of curtailed cricket trousers and shin-guards in a little shed, of going out into a wilderness where touchlines were undreamt of, and where the goal bar fluttered buoyantly in the breeze, where the referee was a casual with a black clay pipe, and a decided impediment in both legs.'

7 Colloquially known as 'the onion bag', **WHAT** was invented by John Alexander Brodie in 1889?

In the mid-1970s the journalist Brian James had an unusual idea. He started with a random FA Cup tie and followed the winning team into the next round until he got to Wembley. When he saw Hednesford Town, James described the place: 'It's an old stable, players wash in a horse trough. The pitch is a bog, cramped and small. The team play 5–4–1 and that's when they are feeling adventurous ... If the walls of that cupboard they call a dressing room could talk, they'd spend the first month reeling off the names of those who had lost there and given up the game forever.' The book by Brian James was called *Tividale to Wembley*.

8 **WHAT** is the title of Lee Howey's autobiography, published in 2018?

Bob Paisley and Bill Shankly were the two most successful managers in the 40 years after the Second World War. Paisley was more introvert, but he could be very thoughtful. 'Some of the jargon is frightening,' said Paisley, in 1980. 'They talk of "getting round the back" and sound like burglars. They say, "You've got to make more positive runs" or "You're too negative". That sounds as though you're filling the team with electricians. But people talk like this without real depth of knowledge of what they're really talking about.'

9 **CAN** you name three other members of the Anfield boot room?

In the 20th century the song 'D'ye Ken John Peel' was still occasionally heard at northern football grounds such as Carlisle United. But there was another John Peel, a disc jockey, musicologist and Liverpool football fan who walked his wife down the aisle to the song 'You'll Never Walk Alone'. 'I flew to Paris for the Real Madrid final with the Liverpool directors, and a more disagreeable bunch of people I've rarely encountered,' said the DJ in 1987.

10 Fred Davies served Shrewsbury Town for 45 years. His record haul was 130 in a season. **WHAT** kind of boat helped?

THE ANSWERS ☞ 150

18

REFEREES (PART 1)

Referees are essential to football. They are the heartbeat of the sport. A referee could be a grey-haired man in his seventies, slightly stooped, his legs working hard to reach the penalty area. Or a stocky man with muscular calves, his midlife crisis hovering, two pencils sticking out of the top of his sock. Or a woman dressed in a yellow shirt and black shorts, her hair in a blonde ponytail as she lopes across the pitch. Or a vicar, in familiar black cloth, known for sending off players for offensive language. The common thread is that they are well-dressed, unbiased, decisive, autonomous, unambiguous in decision-making, and responsible. They know the laws and apply them, but they also recognise the importance of handling players. They concentrate hard and cannot afford to switch off.

1 **WHICH** referee, an alopecia sufferer, wrote the 2003 book *The Rules of the Game*?

In March 2003, two academics, Nick Neave and Sandy Wolfson (Northumbria University), studied the psychological profile of senior referees who averaged 12 years of experience. They found that the referees were cool and confident with nerves of steel and a strong set of coping mechanisms. They were dedicated, committed people who took abuse in their stride and seldom acknowledged being in the wrong. The profile resembled those for police officers, politicians, traffic wardens and military leaders. Top-class referees are fit enough to run about 8 miles (13km) during a game.

2 **WHAT** does OFFINABUS mean to referees?

In 1940, Ken Aston was refereeing a match between RAF Personnel and Low-level Attack Gunners when he saw a German light bomber approaching. Aston abandoned the match, ran to nearby guns, put on a helmet and gas mask, and took to his gun while still wearing his referee's kit. Refereeing involves various other duties: good mental preparation and physical fitness; respect for players and team officials; being honest and impartial; declining matches when not mentally or physically fit; refraining from accepting offers of excessive hospitality; not tolerating inappropriate language; being a gatekeeper to the best interests of football; protecting the players; and not publicly criticising assistants or other match officials.

3 **WHICH** objective fitness test is named after the author of *The Aerobics Way*?

In October 1992 Mr C. A. Clark, a Trowbridge and District referee, had a few problems. Mr Clark was down to referee a match between Waldens and Audience Systems, but the white lines were not marked so he had to postpone the match. It was agreed to play at Audience Systems instead, but Mr Clark lost his way to that ground, so the match was played without the referee. Mr Clark was paid for 42 miles at 15 pence a mile and the full fee was recovered from Audience Systems.

4 Until 1996 **WHAT** name was given to assistant referees?

One contender for the most red cards in a match was Ricky Broadley (Mountain Rangers) in a Safeflue Caernorfan & District League Cup tie against Penrhyndeudraeth in January 2010. In the 64th minute the referee was about to caution two opponents when Broadley stamped on one of the players. That brought a red card. Then Broadley threw water at the referee for a second red card, and his third red was for foul and abusive language. A threat against the referee in the clubhouse caused a further charge. Broadley had already been banned from Sunday football for life, and now he faced a two-year ban from Saturday football.

5 Curtis Woodhouse won four England under-21 caps but he retired from full-time professional football when he was 26. **WHAT** other sport did he take up?

Matches have been called off because of health epidemics, burst water mains, bereavements, floodlight failures and temporary blizzards. Abandonments include a burst ball (with no replacement), a broken crossbar, a player's death, unsafe grandstands (especially in windy weather), dog poo on the pitch, security threats, serious injuries and sent-off players refusing to leave the field. Perhaps the most singular postponement came in 1999 when a total eclipse of the sun caused the match between Torquay United and Portsmouth to be rearranged. The match was replayed a week later and ended 0-0.

6 **WHAT** connects the internationals Martin Chivers, John Robertson and Paul Hartley?

Sometimes players went through the fog to inform spectators and entertained fans with ludicrous stories. In the 1997–98 season a Worksop Town goalkeeper was unaware that a match against Lincoln United had been abandoned until the news was announced over the public address system; he just thought that Lincoln weren't attacking much. A similar event befell goalkeeper Richard Siddall (Stocksbridge Steel) in the fog against Witton Albion. The match was abandoned and so was he. When a 1970 England–Scotland under-23 international was terminated, the blizzard was so heavy that one linesman didn't know that the referee had abandoned the game.

7 **HOW** did two players die during an Army Cup Final in Aldershot in April 1948?

This referee was a lifelong Aston Villa fan. Born in Birmingham, he was a linesman for five years from 1951–56 before spending ten years as a top Football League referee. He helped to organise the 1966 World Cup Finals, held in England. In his autobiography, *Made in Birmingham*, he wrote about a game early in his refereeing career, when his watch stopped as the ball hit it. He solved the problem by timing his game by the one on the next pitch. For many years he was also a Labour Member of Parliament and served as Minister of Sport.

8 **WHO** was he?

One day in July 1966, the referee Ken Aston was driving his car through London and thinking about how referees could communicate better with spectators. Aston, FIFA's chief refereeing instructor, had spotted problems in recent matches. Journalists had been confused about whether the Charlton brothers had both been booked during an England–Argentina match, and Rattín (Argentina) had taken an age to leave the field after being sent off. When Aston drove down Wrights Lane, he stopped and looked at the Kensington High Street traffic lights. He had an idea which eventually became a worldwide success.

9 **WHAT** was Ken Aston's idea?

Wrexham fielded a one-armed player against Chester in 1890, but the real pioneer was a one-legged goalkeeper called Gyngell, who played for Maidenhead Norfolkians in the 1900s. In 1907 the FA ruled that a player was allowed to play with a wooden leg as long as there was no danger to opponents. Fifty years later FIFA banned amputees because prosthetics were not part of standard equipment. But the professional 11-a-side game has produced some excellent one-armed role models, such as Héctor Castro (Uruguay) in the 1930 FIFA World Cup Final, Tony Ward (Arlesey Town) in the 1995 FA Vase Final, and Chris Perrior, who played for Walsall and Kidderminster Harriers in the late 1990s. Alf Bond (Middlesex), a one-armed amputee, took charge of the 1956 FA Cup Final.

10 England came second to Turkey in the 2017 EAFA competition; **WHAT** do the letters EAFA stand for?

THE ANSWERS ☞ 151

19

INJURIES

Charles 'Chic' Brodie was born in February 1937. He was a Scotland schoolboy international goalkeeper who played in England for full-time professional clubs. In 1965 Brodie was playing for Brentford when a Millwall fan threw a hand grenade on to the field. The police put the grenade in a sand bucket. Brodie was still playing for Brentford when he damaged his left knee in a match at Colchester United. A muscular dog, small but solid, charged on to the pitch and ran into Brodie, damaging the goalkeeper's left knee. That was his last Football League match, but he played part-time for Margate, Wealdstone and Maidstone United. He became a London taxi driver.

1 While playing for England in the 2006 World Cup Finals, **WHICH** Real Madrid player injured his anterior cruciate ligament [ACL] and missed most of the next season?

Strange football injuries include an infected pimple after shaving a leg. One goalkeeper twisted his ankle after falling over a sign saying, 'no practice in the goalmouth'. Footballers have also tripped over a son's toy car, fallen in a puddle of puppy urine, slipped on the soap when showering, kicked over a jug of boiling water, and tumbled downstairs. Pre-match photo shoots have seen players rick their backs when falling off benches and tripped up by fun-loving team-mates. They've also hit their heads on dressing room ceilings and dropped liniment bottles on their feet. Players injured during the warm-up can be replaced, even when the team sheet has already been submitted.

2 **WHO** has won more caps than any other Wales player?

Steve Morrow suffered an unusual injury after Arsenal's 2-1 Coca Cola Cup Final win against Sheffield Wednesday in 1993. Arsenal captain Tony Adams lifted Morrow on to his shoulders only for Morrow to topple down to the floor and break his arm. A doctor was called, and Morrow was taken off the field on a stretcher. Morrow won 39 Northern Ireland caps. At the professional level, large sums are tied up in insurance, and injuries limit players to eight-year careers on average.

3 **WHICH** England number nine scored against West Germany at Wembley in 1966, his only goal in 28 international appearances?

Play must be stopped immediately for injuries to the head, ribs, chest, neck, fractures and knee ligaments. If a player lies still the injury could be serious, and a player's health and safety is far more important than a football game. One of the difficult things about playing football is the matter of insurance. Matt Paterson was 20 years old when he suffered a horrendous injury playing against Chalfont St Peter in February 2005. His leg was broken in three places, he had three reconstruction operations, and it transpired that his club was without insurance. A benefit night raised £3,000 but he had to give up his job.

4 **WHAT** is the name of the Gibraltarian sports-injury doctor who has worked for Chelsea, West Ham and the England women's football team?

Fabián Espíndola put the ball in the net for Real Salt Lake against LA Galaxy. Then he tried to emulate the American gymnast Shawn Johnson by doing a cartwheel flip with a half-twist on landing. Unfortunately Espíndola's right foot stuck in the turf and he damaged ankle ligaments. Worse still, the 'goal' was disallowed. Galaxy took the free kick quickly and scored at the other end.

5 In 1997–98 **WHICH** club's fans had the mantra 'It's just like watching Brazil' despite losing 6-0 at home to Chelsea, 5-0 at Arsenal and 7-0 at Manchester United? In the FA Cup, though, they beat Bolton Wanderers, Tottenham Hotspur and Manchester United.

In olden days players bled through bandages or dabbed blood away with a sponge. Terry Butcher (England) cut his head in an aerial challenge against Sweden in September 1989. He was stitched at half time but ended the match with his white shirt stained crimson. Faint-hearted television viewers pined for their old black-and-white sets. Jimmy Floyd Hasselbaink (Middlesbrough) suffered a badly cut head against Chelsea in September 2004. He was off the field for ten minutes while the cut was stitched, and he returned to the field with a clean shirt. After half time the referee asked Hasselbaink to change his second shirt as that also had blood on it. So Hasselbaink wore another clean shirt with the name EHIOGU on the back.

6 **WHICH** Carlisle-born player won nine England caps while at Ipswich Town, appeared in the 1981 film *Escape to Victory* and became a BBC Radio Suffolk commentator after difficulties with alcohol abuse? He died in 2018.

In January 1999 an incident in the Arsenal–Sheffield United FA Cup fifth-round tie created a precedent. Lee Morris (Sheffield United) went down with cramp and a colleague kicked the ball out for a token Arsenal throw. When Parlour (Arsenal) threw the ball towards the United goalkeeper, Kanu (Arsenal) collected the ball, set off and crossed for Overmars (Arsenal) to score. The laws of the game were not broken, and the referee correctly allowed the goal, so Arsenal manager Arsène Wenger offered to replay the tie and the FA agreed. Normally replays are allowed only when referees err in their knowledge of the laws (a technical error). FIFA insisted that both clubs signed a declaration, so the winner of the rematch went forward into the next round.

7 **WHICH** is the only team to have won the FA Cup in Yorkshire?

When Yeovil Town played Plymouth Argyle, in August 2004, Graham Coughlin (Plymouth) received treatment for an injury. When play resumed, Lee Johnson (Yeovil) offered to return the ball to goalkeeper Luke McCormick (Plymouth). Johnson kicked the ball nearly

50 yards towards goal, only to find that the goalkeeper had moved to the side. The ball sailed into the net, and the referee had to award Yeovil a goal. Yeovil manager Gary Johnson immediately went over to Williamson to say that his team would concede a goal. From the kick-off, Steve Crawford (Plymouth) was allowed to walk through the Yeovil defence and equalise. Gary Johnson later joked that it was some of the worst defending he'd ever seen from his players.

8 **WHO** were the opponents when non-League Yeovil Town beat a top-division team and became fourth-round giant-killers in 1949?

There are three common questions when former professional footballers meet: Are you still with your wife? Have you got any grandchildren? And how's the knee? An academic study of 284 former professional players by Andy Turner and others considered the long-term impact of injuries (*British Journal of Sports Medicine*, 2000). The report said that knee injuries, particularly cruciate ligament and meniscus injuries, accounted for nearly 49 per cent of all injuries during an eight-year period from 1987–95. Thirty-two per cent reported having surgery on at least one occasion. Of those, 48 ex-players had had knee surgery (including ten joint replacements) and 15 respondents reported hip surgery (including 12 joint replacements). Twenty-eight per cent were taking medication to reduce football-related symptoms such as pain and inflammation. Turner *et al* said that professional football was not only a game but also a disease of the knee.

9 **WHICH** four of these original 12 members of the Football League have never been champions of the top League? Accrington, Aston Villa, Blackburn Rovers,

Bolton Wanderers, Burnley, Derby County, Everton, Notts County, Preston North End, Stoke, West Brom and Wolves.

During a Plymouth–Middlesbrough match in October 1964, a referee received treatment from both trainers after being accidentally kicked in the face. In the space of a month, in 1966, two referees were seriously injured during matches. One was knocked unconscious at Nottingham Forest, and the other tore an Achilles tendon at Oldham. In each case an assistant took over and a volunteer ran the line. During a Nottingham Forest–Wimbledon match in the early 1990s the Forest goalkeeper kicked the ball from his hands and the ball struck the back of the referee's head. Never turn your back on play, Ref!

10 Bobby Moore captained the West Ham United team in 1964. **WHICH** seven members of that winning team had surnames beginning with the letter 'B'?

THE ANSWERS 152

20

KICKS FROM 12 YARDS

The penalty kick was credited to William McCrum, a Milford Everton (now known as Armagh City FC) goalkeeper who, in 1890, persuaded the Irish FA to propose a law to the International Football Association Board (IFAB). The idea was turned down because a law recognising serious infringement within 12 yards of goal admitted the existence of ungentlemanly play. But an event the following season changed their minds. Notts County led Stoke 1-0 in the last seconds of an FA Cup quarter-final when Hendry (Notts County) fisted away a shot with his goalkeeper beaten. Stoke were awarded an indirect free kick, the maximum punishment at the time, and the ball was scrambled away. Notts County won 1-0 and eventually reached the FA Cup Final. Hendry's actions were not in the spirit of the game.

1 The Football League was formed in 1888 with 12 clubs. In 1890 Stoke were relegated. **WHICH** club replaced Stoke?

Goalkeepers are allowed to take penalty kicks. Ernie Scattergood scored three out of three for Derby County in 1913–14 and took them for Bradford Park Avenue in

1921–22 until South Shields goalkeeper Willis Walker saved one. Goalkeepers kick a lot of stationary balls (e.g. goal kicks) and have faced plenty of penalties. Goalkeepers Arthur Birch (Chesterfield) and Fred Craig (Plymouth Argyle) each scored five penalties in the 1920s. Coventry City's full-back and penalty-taker Roy Kirk, deputising in goal for the injured Jim Sanders, took one against Aldershot in 1958. Kirk shot over the bar, but the crowd held on to the ball and stopped Aldershot taking a quick goal kick.

2 **WHICH** player in the South of England won eight England caps and converted 47 out of 48 penalty kicks?

In April 1939 a match between Birmingham and Chelsea was a dire relegation struggle. A Birmingham win would send Chelsea down. Anything else would send Birmingham down. Birmingham were awarded a penalty, but no player wanted to take the kick. Half a minute passed. Eventually Dearson emerged from the conference of players to take the kick. He shot over the crossbar. Birmingham drew 1-1 and were relegated.

3 Bury, Scarborough, Bristol City, Bolton Wanderers, Nottingham Forest, Wrexham and Middlesbrough. **WHY** is this list significant for the 1996–97 season?

Placing the ball on the penalty mark is a problem on windy days. One dramatic penalty occurred in the 75th minute of the 1936 England–Scotland match at Wembley. England led 1-0 when Tommy Walker (Scotland) placed the ball on the mark, but the wind kept blowing the ball away. On his third attempt he took a short run and shot the equaliser. Sixty years later an England–Scotland match was blighted by a similar problem. England led 1-0 after 76 minutes when Scotland were awarded a penalty. As Gary McAllister (Scotland) ran up to take the kick, the ball rolled slightly away from the spot. McAllister kicked the moving ball and goalkeeper Seaman (England) made the save.

4 **HOW** old was Gary McAllister when he won six medals – Worthington Cup Final, FA Cup Final, UEFA Cup Final, Charity Shield, European Super Cup Final and an MBE?

The penalty shoot-out was introduced to European competitions in 1970 and was considered an improvement on the coin-tossing method used previously. Practising such kicks has become important for every club in the world. Some players hit them hard down the middle, others place them in the corner, and there are those who concentrate on fooling the goalkeeper into going the wrong way. But kicks from the penalty mark will occasionally be missed. There is an old joke: 'The coach told me to keep it well away from the goalkeeper, so I put it over the crossbar.'

5 **WHICH** was the most southerly World Cup Final?

Kicks from the penalty mark can test the nerves of the world's greatest players. When Diego Maradona's club, Napoli, met Toulouse of France in the UEFA Cup the scores were 1-1 on aggregate. Toulouse led 4-3 on kicks from the penalty mark when Maradona took the vital kick. The famous left foot swung into action, clipping the ball well wide of the goalkeeper's right hand, but the ball hit a post and came out. Toulouse went through to the next round.

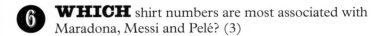

6 **WHICH** shirt numbers are most associated with Maradona, Messi and Pelé? (3)

Jackie Brownsword was a long-serving full-back who played 791 first-team games for Scunthorpe United between 1947 and 1965. A top-class player, he scored 50 out of 51 times from the penalty spot. A miss came in an FA Cup fourth-round replay against Liverpool. 'When Dave Underwood punched away Jack Brownsword's penalty kick there was a groan from the crowd loud enough to be heard in Keadby [5 miles away]' wrote a local journalist. In later life Brownsword worked as Scunthorpe's trainer and, in 1971, helped to facilitate Kevin Keegan's move to Liverpool. In 2016 he was voted into the Professional Football Association's Hall of Fame.

7 **WHICH** Worksop-born full-back was an England manager later in his career?

In the 1950s, two Northern Ireland internationals, Peter Doherty and Danny Blanchflower, practised passing the ball from a penalty. John Newman (Plymouth Argyle) tried it twice in a competitive match. Against Aston Villa, in February 1961, he took Wilf Carter's pass and scored. Against Manchester City, in November 1964, Newman rolled the ball forward for Mike Trebilcock, who only just reached the ball before City goalkeeper Alan Ogley. In September 1966 Bryan Douglas (Blackburn Rovers) worked a similar move with Mike Ferguson. In December 1982 Johan Cruyff (Ajax) played a short forward pass to Jesper Olsen and collected the return to score against Helmond Sport. But it didn't work so well for Arsenal's Robert Pires and Thierry Henry in October 2005. Pires tried to roll the ball sideways but it barely moved, and in the confusion Henry was beaten to the ball.

8 **WHAT** number did Johan Cruyff wear in the 1974 World Cup Finals?

In March 1996, Leicester City manager Martin O'Neill had had only three wins in 16 games. Then came a few good results and they were in the play-off places. Against Crystal Palace, in the last minute of the play-off final, O'Neill took off first-choice goalkeeper Kevin Poole and brought on Zeljko 'Spider' Kalac, who was 6ft 8in (2.03m) and perhaps a more intimidating figure. Then Steve Claridge (Leicester) scored in the last minute, the match ended, and Leicester were promoted to the Premier League before Kalac touched the ball.

9 **WHICH** former Leicester City player once said, 'I've had eleven different clubs, twelve if you count Stringfellows.'

• •

Panenka (Czechoslovakia) won the 1976 European Championship Final by chipping his side's fifth kick over the diving West German goalkeeper. Alan Kennedy (Liverpool) sent the Roma goalkeeper the wrong way to win the 1984 European Cup Final. Roberto Baggio (Italy) shot over the crossbar and his team lost the 1994 FIFA World Cup Final to Brazil. Shoot-outs settled four European Cup Finals in eight years (1984–91), three out of four FIFA World Cup quarter-finals (1986), and both 1990 World Cup semi-finals. In 2004, all three Conference play-off matches were decided by penalties.

10 **WHICH** team won the European Cup in 1961 and 1962 but have since been runners-up in eight major Finals?

THE ANSWERS 153

21

REFEREES (PART 2)

In 2003 assistant referee Morag Pirie met a male chauvinist at Montrose. Peter Hetherston, manager of Albion Rovers, claimed that Pirie 'should be at home making the tea or dinner for her man'. In 2006 another football manager caused a furore. 'She shouldn't be here,' the Luton Town manager said about referee Amy Rayner. 'I know that sounds sexist, but I am sexist, so I am not going to be anything other than that. We have enough problems with political correctness and bringing women into the game is not the way to improve refereeing and officialdom.' His club disassociated itself from his comments. In 2007 Morag Pirie was an assistant referee at the Scottish Challenge Cup Final.

1 **WHAT** name is shared by the director of *Four Weddings and a Funeral* and the Luton Town manager?

When it came to Euro 2008 there was a dearth of female referees. The general list of referees showed that 18.4 per cent of FIFA referees were female, but Euro 2008 had zero female referees, whereas the 1994 World Cup had four. When Silvia Reyes refereed a League match a Uruguayan player accused her of being 'unsatisfied sexually'. The player's comments brought fierce criticism from women's rights' groups and other footballers. In some countries women were not accepted into positions of authority. In 1994 Sonia Denoncourt (Canada) was the first female to be appointed as an international referee, soon followed by Linda Black (New Zealand). Denoncourt refereed the 2000 Olympic Games women's final and the 2003 FIFA Women's World Cup Final.

2 **WHAT** was significant about the officials at a Nationwide Conference match between Kidderminster Harriers and Nuneaton Borough in 1999?

Anything can happen in local football. In the second half, the official referee pulled up and said, 'Me calf's gone.' The referee handed notebook, whistle and watch to a deputy and said they were halfway through the second half, whereupon the manager of the losing team claimed there were still 28 minutes to play. 'I need a pen,' said the home team manager. 'You need to know how to write first,' said a substitute from his team. The home team's manager was all set to referee in T-shirt, sweatpants, trainers and spectacles.

3 Approximately **HOW** many referees are there in England: 10,000, 20,000, 30,000 or 40,000?

Some days everything goes badly for those running the line. An incident on 23 April 1966 affected the relegation places. The Fulham goalkeeper got a hand to the ball and scooped it away. The ball seemed over the line for a goal, but the assistant referee had slipped and fallen over and was no help. It might have been a goal, or it might not have been. One club went down, and the other didn't. Fulham won 4-2 and their opponents felt hard done by.

4 **WHICH** club played in Division 4 (1960–61), Division 3 (1961–62 and 1962–63), Division 2 (1963–64 and 1964–65), Division 1 (1965–66), Division 2 (1966–67), Division 3 (1967–68 and 1968–69) and Division 4 (1969–70)?

The most curious absence of a referee came in March 1948 when Liverpool and Huddersfield Town played the first 30 seconds of the second half without the match official. 'The second half had got nicely under way and the ball was travelling up towards the Liverpool goal, when the 22 players and the crowd suddenly discovered that there was something not quite right about this kind of football,' wrote a local reporter. 'The referee, far from not being on the field, had not even emerged from the tunnel! The roar of amusement which accompanied this false start was one of the most notable I've ever heard.'

5 **WHICH** two clubs in the top four Scottish leagues have a 'V' in their name?

Blackburn Rovers won the 1928 FA Cup Final by beating Huddersfield Town 3-1. The referee for that Final was Tom Bryan, a schoolteacher from Willenhall, Wolverhampton, who oversaw the players in front of 92,041 spectators at Wembley. Bryan had to be level-headed because the next game he refereed was Tarmac v Lane Head United in the Hunt Cup Final. In the 1920s it was a Cup Final tradition for the referee to keep the match ball. Bryan's local club, Whitehall Town, had the ball on display but eventually it was sold to raise money.

6 A Scotsman, a Welshman and an Englishman managed Blackburn Rovers between 2000 and 2008. **WHO** were they?

In September 1981 a referee was suspended for 18 months for punching a player he red-carded at Rhuddlan. In February 1992 a referee with seven years' experience hit a player in the face during a Norfolk Sunday League Division Four match. A similar event in March 1988 occurred during an Andover & District Sunday League match between Southampton Arms and Hurstbourne Tarrant British Legion. The referee eventually produced a red card for himself and walked off the pitch. In a 1995 survey of referees in the West Midlands, John Williams of Leicester University found that 24.5 per cent of referees saw assaults as the most serious problem they faced.

7 **WHICH** Argentina international was sent off against England in a 1966 World Cup quarter-final?

In 1999 Alan Nevill, Nigel Balmer and Mark Williams published a paper on 'homers'. They found that referees watching a videotape with no sound awarded 15.5 per cent fewer fouls to the home team than referees watching with the volume up and crowd noise. But the more experienced the referee, the more balanced the teams became. George Best once summed up the definition of the homer: 'It's human nature, isn't it, if you're a referee? If you go to Leeds and you've got 40,000 people screaming at you, or you go to Liverpool or Old Trafford, you're going to go with the flow. That's what used to happen, and it still does to a certain degree.' Another meaning of 'homer' is the referee who gets home safely after the match.

8 **WHICH** Halifax referee featured in the 1950, 1954 and 1958 World Cups … and, later, in a television knockout competition?

In 'Dehydration of football referees during the match' Da Silva and Fernandez studied a sample of 12 referees in Brazil. The referees suffered moderate dehydration (2.05 per cent of body weight) and it was argued that this could interfere with physical and mental performance. Assistant referees suffered less (1.05 per cent of body weight). These matters came to a head when Jack Charlton's Republic of Ireland team played at noon in 90-degree heat in the United States at the 1994 World Cup Finals. Ireland experimented with water bags, but Ray Houghton was cautioned for having a bag in his hand when the ball came to him. FIFA actively encourages the intake of liquids during a match.

9 **NAME** the four Rangers players in England's 1990 World Cup squad.

He grew up in Wolverhampton over a butcher's shop and was fond of greyhound racing. His main career was as a butcher, but he had a part-time job which eventually took him all around the world. He reached the top level when he officiated in a World Cup Final, but something was missing when he was about to start the match. His other highlights were the 1966 FA Cup Final and the 1971 European Cup Final. Between 1979 and 1982 he was a commercial manager at a football club for three years. He is commemorated in a room at the national football centre near Burton-upon-Trent.

10 **(A) WHAT** was the butcher's name? And **(B) WHAT** was missing when the match was about to start?

THE ANSWERS ☞ 154

22

GHOST GOALS

Two incidents have affected Reading Football Club. In August 1975 a 25-yard shot from Reading's Tommy Youlden put his side one up against Rochdale, despite the ball being on the wrong side of the netting. In the second, in September 2008, the assistant referee flagged for a goal and the match referee agreed for some unknown reason. The incident brought comments such as 'embarrassing' and 'a monumental howler'. The *Guardian*'s John Ashdown commented that 'it was not so much an advert for the introduction of goal-line technology as a rousing endorsement for regular eye tests'.

1 Around the world it can be *cano*, *janelinka*, *poorten*, *petit pont*, *koteny*, *mata nuki*, *kolo*, *bacak arasi*, *beinschuss* … but **WHAT** do they say in England?

In September 1980 Coventry City hosted Crystal Palace. The home side led 3-1 when Palace pulled one back. Clive Allen (Crystal Palace) hit a rocket shot into the goal and the ball rebounded from the stanchion at the back of the net. Then, amazingly, the match continued with the ball in play. The Palace manager,

Terry Venables, managed his rage quietly during the post-match interviews: 'I was disgusted by that decision today,' said Venables. 'We went one up, then we made a couple of individual mistakes and we'd been playing very well. We got the goal to get us back in the game and he disallows it, when there's not even a doubt in my eyes that that went in and hit the iron stanchion at the back.'

2 In the 2004–05 season **WHICH** Crystal Palace player scored more than half of his team's goals – 21 out of 41?

Leigh Griffiths, a Scotland international, once scored a brilliant free kick which hit the bar and bounced down well over the line. Cristiano Ronaldo produced an astonishing overhead kick which hit the bar and then bounced beyond the goal line. And, when Pedro Mendes (Tottenham Hotspur) volleyed the ball from near the halfway line, Manchester United goalkeeper Roy Carroll scrambled the ball away when it was two feet over the goal line. All three goals were wrongly disallowed.

3 During **WHICH** post-war season did Arsenal not lose a League match?

In 1966 England beat West Germany 4-2 at Wembley after extra time. The third England goal was contentious. It was 2-2 when Geoff Hurst swivelled and shot. The ball hit the underside of the bar, bounced down around the line and spun back into play. Roger Hunt, the nearest Englishman, was convinced it was a goal and immediately raised his arm. In a recent interview with FIFA TV, Geoff Hurst spoke about how a manager has to say something important during the break before extra time. Alf Ramsey, the England manager, got the players on their feet and said, 'You've beaten the Germans once, go and beat them again.'

4 Bobby Charlton answered questions on pop music and won the top prize on *Double Your Money* in 1959, but **WHO** won the Bobby Charlton skills competition at the age of 11 in 1986?

Forty-four years after England's World Cup win, Germany beat England 4-1 in the 2010 World Cup Finals. However, when the score was 2-1 to Germany, Frank Lampard shot from about 20 yards. The ball hit the crossbar and bounced down about 2ft over the line. The referee and his assistant were some distance away, so Germany's goalkeeper quickly collected the ball, kicked it down the field and got on with the game. England lost 4-1. Lampard was left with his hands on his head. He knew a goal should have been given.

5 **WHAT** nationality were referee Jorge Larrionda and his assistant referee Mauricio Espinosa when England lost 4-1 to Germany in 2010?

One 'over-the-line' incident was the 1932 FA Cup Final between Arsenal and Newcastle United. Arsenal were missing Alex James, the Scotland international, but they'd won the League that year while Newcastle had finished fifth. Arsenal took a 1-0 lead when Bob John headed in Alex Hulme's centre. Then came the controversy. Did Newcastle's Boyd take the ball over the line before crossing for the equaliser? Photographs and cinema footage suggested that Boyd did. The Arsenal goalkeeper and four team-mates raced to the referee, who had witnessed the event from 20 yards out. The nearest linesman was badly placed. Newcastle went on to win the Cup Final 2-1.

6 **WHICH** army major managed Panathinaikos to the 1971 European Cup Final?

Two types of refereeing error affect 'ball over the line' incidents: (i) the ball that hits the underside of the crossbar and bounces behind the line before it spins back into play; and (ii) where the ball has not gone over the line, but the referee gives a goal. How many assistant referees are in a good place to see along the goal line? At Anfield in 2005 Luis Garcia scored the only goal of a European semi-final (for Liverpool against Chelsea) but did the ball fully cross the line? 'The better side did not win this game,' Chelsea manager Jose Mourinho said. 'The better team is not going to the final. The team that deserves to go is not Liverpool.'

7 **WHAT** do these footballers have in common? Ian Bowyer, Stan Cullis, Dave Hickson, Rob Jones, John Kirkham, Joe Mercer, Graham Turner and Neil Whatmore?

Sheffield Wednesday played Huddersfield Town in a 1930 FA Cup semi-final in front of 70,000 people. Huddersfield led 2-1 in added time when Wednesday's Jack Allen shot towards Huddersfield's goal. The referee blew his whistle for full-time while Allen was in the act of shooting. The ball found the net, but no goal was allowed. The crowd and players were confused. Spectators had to buy a newspaper on the way home to check whether the score was 2-1 or 2-2. Imagine leaving a semi-final on the final whistle and not knowing the result.

8 **WHICH** four clubs beginning with the letter 'W' were knocked out at the FA Cup semi-final stage between 2001 and 2016 (inclusive)?

During the Second World War the state of goal nets was poor. In October 1941, Rochford 'scored' for Portsmouth, but Brentford players complained that the ball had gone through a hole in the roof of the net. The teams were taken off the pitch while the net was repaired. However, when Portsmouth's Guthrie took a penalty later in the game, Sam Bartram, Brentford's wartime goalkeeper, collected the ball from outside the net. Portsmouth players protested that the ball had gone into the net and out through another hole.

9 **WHAT** role in football was filled by, among others, Noel Cantwell, Terry Neill, Derek Dougan, Alan Gowling, Steve Coppell, Brian Talbot, Garth Crooks OBE, Brian Marwood and Pat Nevin?

Not once, but twice. The first moment came in January 1993 when Dundee United's Paddy Connolly's shot crossed the line. It hit a stanchion and bounced out. Partick defender Martin Clark caught the ball and threw it to his goalkeeper, Andy Murdoch, knowing that it was a goal. But the referee played on and most people in the ground were baffled. Fortunately Dundee United won that one. Twenty-five years later Partick Thistle's Kris Doolan shot from the edge of the Morton penalty area, the ball clipped the crossbar and rippled the net for a clear goal. The referee discussed it with his assistant and awarded a throw-in.

10 **WHICH** young Dundee United player scored 46 goals in 62 appearances before moving to England in 1975?

THE ANSWERS ☞ 155

23

MISCELLANEOUS 2

About 20 traditional lawless games are reprised annually from previous centuries. They include those at Atherstone (Warwickshire), Alnwick (Northumberland), Kirkwall (the Orkneys), Ashbourne (Derbyshire) and Workington (Cumbria). The participants battle steamily across fields and through streets, becks and rivers. The games are mammoth rugby scrums. 'It's like watching Lionel Messy,' quipped journalist Brian Daniel, reporting for the *Newcastle Journal* in 2015. The annual Atherstone game in Warwickshire has been played for over 800 years. In the past some players have been seriously injured or drowned.

1 **NAME** the last five clubs to win the English League Championship for the first time?

Twenty-six people were killed and hundreds injured when a section of Ibrox Park terracing collapsed on 5 April 1902. The injured were groaning in the dressing rooms, and players had to step over dead bodies to reach the pitch. The Scotland and England footballers had to play football despite all the groans and yells.

'This may seem strange, but out of the 60,000 present,' wrote C.B. Fry. 'I make bold to say that not more than a thousand were aware of the fact that there had been a serious accident until they reached Glasgow.'

2 **NAME** the last five clubs to win the Scottish League Championship for the first time?

Some people cannot resist a bet. Ever since the pools companies were launched, in the 1920s and 1930s, people have been betting on football results. During the 1950s about 14 million people regularly connected with football through the ritual of completing a pools coupon. The classified results were read out with the resonance of an epic poem, and men and women checked their home wins, away wins and draws. Keith Nicholson's big pools win was either good news or bad news. Nicholson died in a car crash when he was 27.

3 **HOW** much did Keith Nicholson win in the pools in September 1961? Was it **(A)** £4,458; **(B)** £34,837; **(C)** £56,312; **(D)** £92,117; or **(E)** £152,319?

In August 2015 a man bet £5 on five away teams winning, and sure enough they all did. Crystal Palace won 2-1 at Chelsea, West Brom won 1-0 at Stoke City, West Ham won 3-0 at Liverpool, Cardiff City won 2-1 at Nottingham Forest, and Leeds United won 2-1 against Derby County. Leeds relied on an 88th-minute winner by Chris Wood.

4 **HOW** much did the man win? **(A)** £10,000; **(B)** £20,000; **(C)** £30,000; or **(D)** £40,000?

In 1952–53 the amateur team Walthamstow Avenue reached the FA Cup fourth round. After beating Wimbledon in a first-round replay and Watford in a second-round replay, the Avenue had a third-round tie against Stockport County. 'I don't know where the pass came from,' said Dickie Lucas, after he'd scored the winner against Stockport. 'The ball dropped at my feet from nowhere, and I coshed it for all it was worth.' The run continued with a 1-1 draw at Manchester United's Old Trafford in front of 35,000 spectators before United won comfortably 5-2 in the replay, watched by 46,000 at Highbury. Some people wondered where the money went. There were tales of money being left in football boots after matches and jokes about amateurs being paid more than the professionals.

5 **WHICH** English club and Welsh club met in the FA Cup third round at the same ground in three successive seasons – 1956, 1957 and 1958 – with the same result each time?

During the period between 1966 and 1982 four different Southampton strikers finished as top goal scorers in the English League's top division. The Welshman had a party piece of drawing caricatures, and he was top goal scorer in consecutive years, first on his own and then jointly with a famous international player. Another striker, in the early 1970s, had a party piece of training racehorses, and a third was once given a free transfer by Brian Clough. The fourth was the smallest and perhaps the most famous.

6 **WHAT** were the names of the four Southampton strikers? (4)

After 40 minutes of a match between Bradford City and Lincoln City, on 11 May 1985, a fire broke out in G Block of the wooden main stand at Valley Parade. Spectators spilled on to the pitch, and the referee stopped the match. Fifty-six people were killed and more than 250 injured. Some crucial Guide to Safety at Sports Grounds regulations were not in place at Bradford. There was no dedicated person in charge, exit gates were closed, and building materials could have been safer. The fire was believed to have been caused by a lighted cigarette being dropped through a gap in the wooden floorboards. It fell on debris that had collected beneath the stand over many years. The 0-0 scoreline stood as a result.

7 Fourteen years after the fire Bradford City spent two seasons in the Premier League (1999–2000 and 2000–01). Another 12 years passed before Bradford City had a sensational League Cup run, defeating **WHICH** three Premier League clubs *en route* to the Final? (3)

Many club nicknames are long-standing, and their origins can range from the obvious to the uncertain. In Portsmouth, for instance, sailors told tales. One theory was that Aggie Weston, who ran a Portsmouth hostel for sailors, gave a talk around 1904 about a Roman General called Pompey the Great. As she was talking, a sailor shouted, 'Poor old Pompey,' and football fans took up the chant. But the nickname could have arisen from a Royal Artillery team returning from a tour of duty in France and cheering for 'les Pompiers' (the French for firemen). Or it could have been another story.

8 **WHICH** Test cricketer and sportsman played for Southampton in all seven FA Cup ties when the club reached the Final in 1902?

Here come the Rowley brothers. On 22 October 1955 Arthur scored his 200th League goal after 53 minutes at Fulham, and, on the same day, elder brother Jack scored his 200th League goal after 65 minutes at Barnsley. In November 1943 Wolves beat Derby 8-1 and Jack scored all eight. After the war Arthur played for Fulham and Leicester City. He became Shrewsbury Town's player-manager and chalked up 434 League goals in 619 matches during his career, an unbeatable figure. Jack scored 211 goals in 424 peacetime outings with Manchester United and won six England international caps. Jack also managed Plymouth Argyle, Oldham Athletic (twice), Ajax Amsterdam, Wrexham and Bradford Park Avenue. He later worked as a newsagent and ran a post office near Oldham. Arthur worked for Vernon's Pools.

9 Jack Rowley was one of four players to score 200 goals for Manchester United. **WHO** were the other three?

When Middlesbrough played Crystal Palace, in August 1968, the Middlesbrough players protested that the two strips clashed. One team returned to the dressing room for a quick change. In February 1979 a referee ordered a change at half time when Swindon Town (white shirts and red shorts) played at Rotherham United (red shirts and white shorts). There were difficulties when Cambridge United (yellow shirts, black shorts and yellow socks) played Oxford United (black shirts, yellow shorts and black socks). In the days of black-and-white television sets it was difficult to distinguish between red and blue. In 1978, one World Cup game was delayed by 40 minutes while a set of shirts were borrowed.

10 **WHOSE** ground is closest to the River Mersey: Everton, Liverpool, Stockport County or Tranmere Rovers?

THE ANSWERS 156

24

WHO ARE THEY? (PART 2)

On 24 March 2007 this footballer played for England under-21s against Italy under-21s. He could smell the fresh paint at Wembley and he admired the grass surface. Italy scored after 25 seconds and then he equalised from a 25-yard free kick, the first England player to score at the rebuilt Wembley stadium. He was also the first to score a Premier League hat-trick against Manchester United. He won seven England caps in 2007–08 and was one of four players to play for Arsenal and Tottenham Hotspur in the Premier League. But he retired early. He worked in sports management and ran bars and restaurants in Marbella.

1 **WHO** is he?

Central Park had greyhound racing in the 1950s. In 1957 the club's supporters' association planned a new covered enclosure at the Chapel Street end of the ground. In 1965 the greyhound racetrack was replaced by a speedway dirt track. The floodlights were erected in 1968, and Jock Stein, manager of Celtic, reckoned the lights were better than those at some top-flight Scottish grounds. The 'Coo-shed', as it became known, could hold 2,000 fans but it had to be removed in the early 1980s. The club's nickname is the Blue Brazil.

2 **WHAT** is the name of the club?

He and his mate Blackie Gray left their youth club team and signed for the Rovers. It was a simple story at first. Then he was disappointed to be left out of the 1966 World Cup squad. Penny was a secretary at the football club and she married her husband in 1976. A year later the couple had twins (a girl and a boy). Their third child, Diana, arrived in 1982, when that Christian name was popular. They were a homely couple at heart but inevitably he took the limelight because he was a great player. He scored 533 goals in 565 games for club and country, and he won nine League titles, eight FA Cups and three European Cups.

3 **WHO** was he?

He was a cheerleader for various events, including sporting occasions. During a 1939 Atlantic crossing on the SS *Bremen*, he was one of four men who ran 997 miles (1,604km) around the ship's deck in five and a half days. He carried a torch at the 1948 Wembley Olympics and wrote columns for the *Bournemouth Times*. He wore a red coat and black top hat, and he became a mascot during the 1966 World Cup Finals. On another occasion, in January 1982, a 24-year-old streaker, Erica Roe, ran on to the Twickenham pitch during a rugby international. The cheerleader with the red coat waved his Union Jack flag to conceal her top half. He also turned up as a mascot in Subbuteo, especially in the 1960s and 1970s, when about 300,000 Subbuteo sets were sold annually. A Subbuteo World Cup was founded in 1987, black Subbuteo players arrived in the 1990s and then computer games started to take over.

4 **WHO** was he?

This club joined the Scottish League in 1923–24 and finished the season with four wins and 20 defeats. The club often finished bottom as it was hard to sustain a good team in a town of about 7,000 people. In 2018 they became the first Scottish team since 1892 to end a season without a win. 'I just keep smiling,' said 89-year-old fan Margaret Noble, 'You've got to. I live on my own, my daughter is in America and my son is in Dorset. The club is my family.' In a BBC Scotland spoof documentary, the club was apparently the first to dabble in sponsorship when the locals offered the club money to play somewhere else.

5 **WHICH** club is it?

In 1981–82 he scored 289 goals in 40 League and Cup matches for Bolton Lads Club. He scored in every game and reached double figures in six matches, including 16 in one match and 15 in another. Like his father, Anthony, he was born in Farnworth and signed as a Manchester City apprentice. The son, Paul, scored 46 goals in 183 appearances for seven clubs, including Manchester City, Birmingham City and Oldham Athletic. Paul later coached Manchester City's academy players and Bolton Lads Club. He needed two new hips because of his football career and went on to run a fish and chip shop in Bolton called Paul's Chippy.

6 **WHAT** was Anthony and Paul's surname?

Still a current Premiership manager in 2018, his autobiography *The Gaffer* came out in 2013. He played for eight clubs, only one of them south of Chesterfield, and has managed 15 clubs over a period of almost 40 years. He took a team from the Conference to League Two, another from League One to the Premiership, and two other clubs from the Championship to the Premiership.

7 **WHO** is he?

Once upon a time there was a father (Jess), a son (Roy) and a nephew (Phil). Between them they made over 1,200 League appearances for the Vale, and Roy is commemorated by a statue outside the Staffordshire ground. Roy was also part of a 46-game Iron Curtain defence which achieved 30 clean sheets in the 1953–54 season. That season the team conceded only four in an eight-game FA Cup run, ended in the semi-final by a dubious West Brom penalty. Roy managed the club for nearly four years from January 1974 to October 1977.

8 **(A) WHO** does the statue depict; and **(B) WHAT** links Mark Grew, Ian Taylor, Neil Aspin, Martin Foyle, Jon McCarthy, Lee Mills and Gareth Ainsworth between 1992 and 1998 (inclusive)?

In September 1975 this man played in a County Championship cricket match for Leicestershire against Derbyshire and, on the same day, a professional football match for Doncaster Rovers. He was 51 not out when he changed into football kit and played in a 1-1 draw 30 miles away. The next day he returned to Chesterfield, completed his century and took three wickets to wrap up Leicestershire's first-ever County Championship title. He was a right-handed bat and left-arm spinner, and he played in two Tests against the West Indies. He played 566 Football League games and scored 93 goals, and he once put on 289 with David Gower. He played cricket for Leicestershire until 1986.

9 **(A) WHICH** Huddersfield Town manager signed this cricketer-footballer to his first football contract? And **(B)** What was the player's name?

Born in Scarborough, this man scored after 19 seconds of his first – and only – England international match. They'd hardly kicked off when Stan Pearson headed the ball back and he scored with his first touch. He won nine major trophies, all except one as a manager. He had 36 years at Tottenham, including 16 as manager. He was team coach from 1955 and helped England manager Walter Winterbottom at the 1958 World Cup Finals. Spurs won 10-4 against Everton in one game and 13-2 against Crewe Alexandra in a 1960 FA Cup replay (10-0 at half time). He had three FA Cup triumphs in seven years during the 1960s. He lived in a modest house near the White Hart Lane ground with his wife and family.

10 **WHO** was he?

THE ANSWERS 157

25

INTO EUROPE

Everton's T.G. Jones was manager of Bangor City during the 1961–62 season. His team were drawn against Napoli in a European match, so he paid for a trip to Naples, watched his opponents and sought advice from English footballers in Italy. T.G. Jones told his players, 'You are not only playing for Bangor City, tonight you are also representing Wales.' Bangor won the home leg 2-0, helped by spectators. 'The result caught the public imagination in the UK and far beyond,' wrote Rob Sawyer in *The Prince of Centre Halves*. Napoli won the second leg 3-1; a third match, played at Arsenal's Highbury Stadium, ended 2-1 to Napoli.

1 Danny Wilson, father of Ryan Giggs, won five caps for Wales: **(A)** in **WHICH** sport? **(B)** with **WHICH** team?

Newcastle United won the Inter Cities Fairs Cup in 1969. They knocked out Feyenoord (Rotterdam), Sporting Club de Portugal, Real Zaragoza, Vitória de Setúbal, Glasgow Rangers and Újpest Dosza. In the final Newcastle won the first leg 3-0 and the second 3-2. Bobby Moncur, Newcastle's sweeper and captain, scored three goals in those two matches and his goals were very rare. He scored from close range, added a second after running from the centre circle and, in the second leg, scored with a left-footed volley.

2 **WHICH** future England international made his first 51 professional appearances for an Irish club managed by his father before joining Newcastle United?

'Beckham, into Sheringham, and Solskjær has won it,' commentated Clive Tyldesley on 25 May 1999. 'Nobody will ever win a European Cup Final more dramatically than this – champions of Europe, champions of England, winners of the FA Cup.' Manchester United were 1-0 down after 90 minutes and Bayern Munich were controlling the match. Then Teddy Sheringham turned in an equaliser after 36 seconds of added time, and Ole Gunnar Solskjær scored the winner 100 seconds later. Peter Schmeichel, the Manchester United goalkeeper and captain, was doing somersaults. When interviewed after the match United manager Alex Ferguson said, 'Football, eh, bloody hell.' Ferguson was knighted 17 days after the triumph in Barcelona.

3 **WHICH** two Manchester United players missed the final through suspension?

Between 1986 and 2009 Vic Akers was manager of the Arsenal women's team. Arsenal won the FA Women's Cup 11 times, the FA Premier League 11 times and the Women's Premier League Cup ten times. In 2006–07 Arsenal became the first English team to win the UEFA Women's Cup, winning 1-0 away to Umeå and drawing 0-0 in the second leg in England. The only goal of the final came in added time of the first match, when full-back Alex Scott ran forward and hit a screamer from

25 yards into the top-left corner. Scott won 140 England international caps in her career.

4 **WHAT** is the only women's name to appear in the League tables?

In July and August 2018 Burnley played six European matches. They beat Aberdeen and Istanbul Başakşehir but lost to Olympiacos. Their previous European adventures had occurred in the 1960–61 and 1966–67 seasons, the first after Burnley had been League Champions for the second time in their history. Stars from that era included forward John Connolly. Connelly played for three other North West clubs – Manchester United, Blackburn Rovers and Bury – and altogether made 622 appearances and scored 200 goals. In later life he ran a fish and chip shop called Connelly's Plaice.

5 John Connelly was the third member of the 1966 England squad to die. **WHO** were the first two?

In 1909 football teams from Italy, Germany, Switzerland and England were chosen for the Sir Thomas Lipton Trophy. The competition, held in Turin (Italy), was treated as a World Cup. The West Auckland team, all amateurs, mainly coal miners, won the trophy. Two years later they won again, beating Juventus 6-1 in the Final. West Auckland Town folded in 1912 and re-formed in 1914. A hundred years later the club reached two FA Vase Finals at Wembley (2012 and 2014), losing to Dunstan UTS and Sholing. West Auckland reached the FA Cup first round twice, losing to Barnsley in a replay (in 1961–62) and Yeovil Town after a replay and a penalty shoot-out (in 1998–99).

6 Ronnie Radford and Ricky George were wearing consecutive numbers when they scored their two famous FA Cup goals for Hereford United. **WHAT** were the numbers?

'Mortimer, Shaw, Williams, prepared to venture down the left,' commentated Brian Moore on 26 May 1982. 'There's a good ball played in for Tony Morley, oh, it must be, and it is! It's Peter Withe, Villa in the lead.' Aston Villa scored the only goal of the game and brought England a sixth successive European Cup trophy, following Liverpool (three times) and Nottingham Forest (twice). Villa goalkeeper Nigel Spink replaced the injured Jimmy Rimmer in the ninth minute and made four excellent saves. The Villa manager was Tony Barton, who had recently taken over from Ron Saunders.

7 **HOW** many senior appearances had Spink made before the European Cup Final? Was it **(A)** 1, **(B)** 27, **(C)** 44, **(D)** 62 or **(E)** 89?

In 1986 Oxford United beat Queen's Park Rangers 3-0 in the Milk Cup Final. Oxford led 1-0 at half time and manager Maurice Evans, as he walked off the pitch, saw a Milk Marketing Board slogan and used it. 'Have you got the bottle to win it?' Evans asked his players in the dressing room. 'Because that is all you need.' In normal circumstances Oxford would have been in European competition but English clubs had been banned for five years (1985 to 1990). Strangely the only person who had played in European club football was Ken Fish, Oxford United's long-serving trainer and physiotherapist. Fish had been with the Swiss club Young Boys in the late 1930s.

8 **WHICH** football ground straddles two FIFA member countries?

Tottenham Hotspur played 12 matches in the 1983–84 UEFA Cup competition. The Spurs manager was Barnsley-born Keith Burkinshaw, whose career included an eight-year period at Spurs. A 1-1 draw in the first leg at Anderlecht set up the match at White Hart Lane ('White Hot Lane' in those days). Another 1-1 draw led to extra time and a penalty shoot-out. The second Anderlecht kick was saved, but Danny Thomas (Spurs) missed the ninth and then the fans sang 'There's only one Danny Thomas'. On the tenth kick, goalkeeper Tony Parks flung himself to his right and clawed the ball away. Spurs players charged up the pitch and threw themselves into a pyramid.

9 During the 2008 Carling Cup Final between Chelsea and Tottenham Hotspur all three goal scorers were wearing headbands. Can you name them?

In 1979 Ipswich Town manager Bobby Robson signed two Dutch players, Frans Thijssen and Arnold Mühren. Paul Mariner and Alan Brazil were the main strikers, Paul Cooper was the goalkeeper and Mick Mills captain. John Wark scored 14 goals (including six penalties) and Ipswich Town won the UEFA Cup in 1980–81. St Etienne had Johnny Rep and Michel Platini in their quarter-final, but Ipswich won 7-2 on aggregate. Two 1-0 wins saw off FC Cologne, and AZ Alkmaar were beaten 5-4 on aggregate. Manager Bobby Robson and assistant Bobby Ferguson oversaw it all.

10 **WHAT** is Ipswich Town's recent nickname, coined around the end of the 20th century?

THE ANSWERS 158

THE ANSWERS

1

THE ANSWERS

STREAKERS

1. May 2004
2. (d)
3. Queen of the South
4. Gareth Bale (Wales)
5. £769 (a £500 fine for indecent exposure, £200 for the pitch invasion and £69 court costs).
6. *Playboy*.
7. ‘Superbowel’; he does it because he enjoys hearing the laughter.
8. Second in the top flight.
9. The tattoo was ‘Glentoran 1882 – le jeu avant tout’ (‘the game comes first’).
10. He was a police officer.

2

THE ANSWERS

MASCOTS

1. Once
2. Jermaine Defoe
3. *Marvellous*; Toby Jones.
4. Torquay United, Oldham Athletic and Cheltenham Town.
5. David Shrigley
6. Seventeen were arrested (and over 20 injured).
7. Watford, Bristol Rovers and Scunthorpe United.
8. Football's Furry Friends.
9. Blue and white.
10. Goaliath

3

THE ANSWERS

OUTLANDISH SCORELINES

1. 459 consecutive appearances for Tranmere Rovers.

2. Third Lanark

3. Motherwell and Hibernian.

4. Australia beat American Samoa 31-0.

5. Gerry Hitchens

6. Madagascar

7. No wins in eight finals.

8. 'For he's a jolly good fellow'

9. Everton

10. The City players were numbered 12–22, whereas opponents Everton were more traditional, wearing 1–11.

4

THE ANSWERS

LONG-RUNNING SAGAS

1. Old Trafford had the highest crowd for the fifth match (22,549).
2. Belle Vue had the highest crowd in the first match (27,707).
3. Graham Allner
4. (a) Denmark, (b) Denmark.
5. Dixie Deans
6. Ted Drake, Tom Finney, George Young, Arthur Ellis and Tommy Lawton.
7. Eric Morecambe
8. Eleven
9. Grimsby Town
10. (a) Unexpected blizzard, (b) Spurs wore all white and couldn't be seen, (c) assistant referees couldn't see across the pitch, (d) hazardous conditions underfoot, (e) forecast was terrible.

5

THE ANSWERS

SINGING AND CHANTING

1. 'Abide with Me'
2. Danny Blanchflower
3. England 2, Colombia 0.
4. Knowles
5. Paper Lace
6. Barcelona
7. Ian Storey-Moore
8. 'On the ball, City' (Norwich City).
9. The Mismanagement Committee
10. Des O'Connor

6

THE ANSWERS

THE JOKERS

1. Joey Barton

2. Leyton Orient

3. Wendy Toms

4. Palestine

5. Johnny Haynes and George Cohen.

6. Gordon Banks

7. Netherlands, Hungary and Norway.

8. League appearances: Wark (611), Euell (427) and Gary Neville (400); international caps: Gary Neville (85), Wark (29) and Euell (3).

9. Alan Hodgkinson, Eddie Hopkinson and Colin McDonald.

10. Someone took a corner.

7

THE ANSWERS

FLOODLIGHTS

1. The Dell, Southampton.
2. AFC Fylde, Dagenham & Redbridge and Havant & Waterlooville.
3. Leeds United
4. Morpeth Town's nickname is the Highwaymen, and the other four played in a band called The Highwaymen.
5. Brazil
6. Stefano Eranio
7. Truro City
8. Stade Louis II (Monaco)
9. Peterborough United
10. Aldershot

8

THE ANSWERS

PROFESSIONAL FOOTBALL

1. Father and son managers.
2. We don't know!
3. He bought Gascoigne a toilet brush.
4. Ruud van Nistelrooy
5. Huddersfield Town
6. *Z Cars*.
7. (b), (c) and (d)
8. Bob Paisley
9. The Hive
10. Craig Shakespeare

9

THE ANSWERS

TRAVEL TALES

1. 7,474
2. Rory Delap
3. Purple
4. (a)
5. The Lion of Vienna
6. Bobby Moore (1966), Paul Gascoigne (1990), Michael Owen (1998), David Beckham (2001) and Ryan Giggs (2009).
7. Trevor Brooking. (Alan Sunderland, Brooking and Ricardo Villa all scored the winning goals in FA Cup Finals.)
8. Frank Clark. The club was known as Orient (until 1987) and Leyton Orient (after 1987).
9. England v Italy (1934), Hungary v Brazil (1954), Italy v Chile (1962), Harold Godwinson v Harold Hardrada (1066).
10. Trevor Ford

10

THE ANSWERS

THE LAWS OF ASSOCIATION FOOTBALL

1. They were all seriously injured in FA Cup Finals.
2. (e)
3. The Diagonal System of Control.
4. Seven
5. Denial of Obvious Goal Scoring Opportunity.
6. Aston Villa, Charlton Athletic, Liverpool, Northampton Town and York City.
7. (c)
8. Busby one, McGuinness two.
9. It was the first professional match played on a Sunday. Admission was free, and spectators purchased a programme for the price of a ticket.
10. Usain Bolt

11

THE ANSWERS

MATHEMATICS AND STATISTICS

1. Ards, Rhyl and Bury.

2. Roberto Carlos

3. (f)

4. Bury

5. Kenny Hibbitt scored for Wolves in the first half and Terry Hibbitt scored for Newcastle United in the second half.

6. Eight

7. Carragher, Cissé, Finnan, Gerrard, Hamann, Hyypiä, Kewell, Riise and Sissoko.

8. Dundee.

9. Reviews include: (a) violations of play during an attacking phase before a goal (e.g. offside or a foul), (b) penalty decisions, (c) direct red cards (but not second yellows), and (d) mistaken identity in awarding a red or yellow card.

10. Alan Hinton 17 (including eight penalties), Kevin Hector 15, Alan Durban 10, John O'Hare 13 and Frank Wignall five.

12

THE ANSWERS

WARTIME FOOTBALL

1. Fourth of July.
2. The Falkland Islands national team.
3. The number of corner kicks and tossing a coin.
4. Preston
5. Ian Buxton
6. Norway
7. (d)
8. The game was featured in the 1981 film *Escape to Victory*.
9. Thirty-nine steps.
10. The news was being read.

13

THE ANSWERS

STRANGE INCIDENTS

1. Derek Dougan

2. The BBC organised a competition for best commentator, several auditioned and a few commentated on a segment of the game. John Motson was voted the winner.

3. 'There's only two Gary Stevens'.

4. £400

5. He scored all four goals in a 2-2 draw – two for Leicester City and two own goals for Aston Villa.

6. Aberdeen and Dundee United.

7. Three

8. Cambridge United

9. Kieran Dyer, Michael Flanagan and David Batty.

10. Grimsby Town and Wolverhampton Wanderers in an FA Cup semi-final. Wolves beat Grimsby Town 5-0.

14

THE ANSWERS

WHO ARE THEY? (PART 1)

1. Mel Sterland
2. Graham Alexander
3. Ernie Hunt
4. Jeff Astle
5. R.S. McColl
6. Tom 'Tiny' Wharton
7. Two teams of deaf footballers.
8. Dion Dublin
9. Alan and Les Sealey.
10. Andrés Iniesta

15

THE ANSWERS

MISCELLANEOUS 1

1. Duncan Ferguson (Everton) and Salomón Rondón (West Brom).

2. Football agent

3. England beat Panama 6-1.

4. Pat Howard

5. (a)

6. Queen's Park Rangers and Swindon Town.

7. Brighton & Hove Albion and Lewes.

8. Vinnie Jones. Steve Walsh and Roy McDonough were each sent off 13 times between 1979 and 2001.

9. Raith Rovers

10. Derby

16

THE ANSWERS

WOMEN AND FOOTBALL

1. Eddie Reynolds scored with four headers.

2. Nuneaton Borough

3. Dave Bennett

4. Nellis and Reilly were Scottish.

5. Alan Kennedy

6. Brentford, Cheltenham Town, Exeter City, Lincoln City, Sheffield United, Stoke City, Sunderland.

7. Sian Massey Ellis, MBE

8. Kelly Smith

9. Marta

10. Kristine Lilly

17

THE ANSWERS

QUOTATIONS

1. Imre Varadi

2. The England Women's international team.

3. Crystal Palace, Morecambe, Plymouth Argyle, Port Vale, Rochdale and Stevenage.

4. Carlisle United

5. The Cambridge Rules of football.

6. Tony Kay

7. Goal nets

8. *Massively Violent and Decidedly Average*

9. In the 1980s the key backroom staff were Tom Saunders, Joe Fagan, Ronnie Moran and Reuben Bennett.

10. A coracle. Davies fished stray balls out of the River Severn, which was adjacent to Shrewsbury's old ground, Gay Meadow.

18

THE ANSWERS

REFEREES (PART 1)

1. Pierluigi Collina
2. OFFensive, INsulting or ABUSive language.
3. The Cooper Test
4. Linesmen
5. Boxing
6. Makes of jam.
7. Lightning strikes
8. Denis Howell
9. Red cards for sending-offs and yellow cards for caution.
10. European Amputee Football Association

19

THE ANSWERS

INJURIES

1. Michael Owen

2. Neville Southall

3. Nobby Stiles. This England v West Germany match took place in February 1966.

4. Eva Carneiro

5. Barnsley (at Sheffield's Bramall Lane).

6. Kevin Beattie

7. Barnsley (in 1912).

8. Sunderland

9. Accrington, Bolton, Notts County and Stoke.

10. John Bond, Jack Burkett, Eddie Bovington, Ken Brown, Peter Brabrook, Ronnie Boyce and Johnny Byrne.

20

THE ANSWERS

KICKS FROM 12 YARDS

1. Sunderland
2. Matthew Le Tissier
3. They were the opponents when Chesterfield reached the FA Cup semi-final.
4. Thirty-six years old
5. Montevideo (Uruguay)
6. Ten, ten and ten.
7. Graham Taylor
8. Fourteen
9. Frank Worthington
10. Benfica

21
THE ANSWERS
REFEREES (PART 2)

1. Mike Newell
2. All three officials were women.
3. 30,000
4. Northampton Town
5. Inverness Caledonian Thistle and Livingstone.
6. Graeme Souness, Mark Hughes and Paul Ince.
7. Antonio Rattín
8. Arthur Ellis
9. Gary Stevens, Terry Butcher, Chris Woods and Trevor Steven.
10. (a) Jack Taylor; (b) the corner-flags were missing, and Taylor sorted it out before they could start the match.

22

THE ANSWERS

GHOST GOALS

1. Nutmeg

2 Andy Johnson

3. The 2003–04 season. Arsenal won 26 League matches and drew 12 of their 38 games.

4. David Beckham

5. Uruguayan

6. Ferenc Puskàs

7. They were all born in Ellesmere Port.

8. Wycombe Wanderers (2001), Watford (three times, 2002, 2007, 2016), West Brom (2008) and Wigan Athletic (2014).

9. Chairman of the Professional Footballers' Association.

10. Andy Gray

23

THE ANSWERS

MISCELLANEOUS 2

1. Leicester City (2016), Nottingham Forest (1978), Derby County (1972), Leeds United (1969) and Ipswich Town (1962).

2. Dundee United (1983), Kilmarnock (1965), Dundee (1962), Aberdeen (1955) and Motherwell (1932).

3. (e)

4. (d)

5. Leeds United lost 2-1 to Cardiff City in the third round in three successive seasons.

6. Ron Davies, Mike Channon, Phil Boyer and Kevin Keegan.

7. Wigan Athletic, Arsenal and Aston Villa.

8. C.B. Fry

9. Denis Law, Bobby Charlton and Wayne Rooney.

10. Stockport County

WHO ARE THEY? (PART 2)

1. David Bentley
2. Cowdenbeath
3. Roy Race (Roy of the Rovers)
4. Ken Baily
5. Brechin City
6. Moulden
7. Neil Warnock
8. (a) Roy Sproson; (b) Port Vale player of the year winners.
9. (a) Bill Shankly; (b) Chris Balderstone.
10. Bill Nicholson

25

THE ANSWERS

INTO EUROPE

1. (a) Rugby League; (b) Salford.
2. George Eastham
3. Roy Keane and Paul Scholes.
4. (Crewe) Alexandra
5. Bobby Moore and Alan Ball.
6. Eleven and twelve.
7. One
8. Chester City. The stadium is in England, but the pitch is in Wales.
9. Jonathan Woodgate (Spurs), Dimitar Berbatov (Spurs) and Didier Drogba (Chelsea).
10. The Tractor Boys

'At the end of the day it's not the end of the world.'

Jim McLean,
Dundee United manager,
after UEFA Cup Final defeat,
1987

ABOUT THE AUTHORS

Sports fanatic, journalist and inveterate chronicler of the weird, Andrew Ward is the author of *Football's Strangest Matches*, *Cricket's Strangest Matches*, *Golf's Strangest Rounds* and *Horse Racing's Strangest Races*, all published by Portico.

This is Ian Alister's first collaboration with Andrew Ward since they wrote *Barnsley: A Study in Football, 1953–59* (Crowberry, 1981).